WONDER BOOK
OF THE
WORLD'S PROGRESS

VOL. I
THE UNIVERSE • THE EARTH

DR. FRANCIS G. PEASE MEASURING A STAR

WONDER BOOK

OF THE
WORLD'S PROGRESS

By
HENRY SMITH WILLIAMS

IN TEN VOLUMES
Illustrated

•

VOLUME I
The Universe
The Earth

FUNK & WAGNALLS COMPANY
NEW YORK AND LONDON

INTRODUCTION

I HAVE been gathering material for this set of books for many years. Within the past five years I have published several volumes that incorporated portions of the material which is now for the first time brought together in a unified work. Among these books, upon which I have drawn freely in preparing the present work, are *The Great Astronomers, The History of Science, The Biography of Mother Earth, Survival of the Fittest, Why Die Before Your Time?* and *Drugs Against Men.* Some of my earlier works, including *The History of the Art of Writing* and *The Historians' History of the World,* have also been utilized, and to a less extent numerous other volumes. But of necessity the present series as a whole is unique. It represents an attempt to bring the essentials of progress of natural phenomena and of man's interpretation of the phenomena into a single series of books, which I have looked forward to with eagerness for many years.

In making the endeavor to bring within such relatively small compass so wide a variety of material, it has been necessary to practise before all else the art of selection. What I had in mind is a work as far as possible removed from an encyclopedia — which of necessity covers a multitude of subjects and has less freedom to discriminate between the important and the unimportant. The effort here, on the contrary, has been to make from the outset an interpretation of the value of this or that aspect of knowledge, as compared with other aspects.

The central point is that the presentation, somewhat *in extenso,* of the development of a given form of knowledge during a certain period, has far greater interest and vastly more educational value than an attempt to deal with a multitude of minor events not presented in proper perspective. How this works out in practise will be better understood from scanning the pages themselves than from any more detailed explanation.

It will be seen that great stress is laid on pictorial presentation. Many subjects scarcely referred to in the text are graphically presented in pictures. In not a few instances the effort is made to present, at a glance, the entire perspective of the development of a line of invention or discovery by contrasting crude beginnings with elaborated endings. But here again the pictures had best be left to speak for themselves.

It will be seen that the pictures are drawn from many sources. A very large number of them are from photographs furnished by Brown Brothers, of New York City, whose cooperation in gathering material for illustrations I have enjoyed for the past thirty years. Where some other source is not credited, it will be understood that all the photographs reproduced are copyrighted by Brown Brothers. The owners of the copyright have very courteously consented to cooperate with the publishers by accepting this credit in lieu of the usual copyright notice in connection with each picture.

The author wishes to express his obligation to various publishers of his earlier books, including Messrs. Harper & Brothers, the Encyclopedia Britannica Company, the Goodhue Company, Simon & Schuster, and Thomas M. McBride & Company, for permission to draw freely on material incorporated in books issued by them.

H. S. W.

CONTENTS — VOL. I

THE UNIVERSE · THE EARTH

I

THE NEW HEAVENS

Lift up your eyes to the heavens, and look upon
the earth beneath: for the heavens shall vanish
away like smoke, and the earth shall wax old
like a garment.— *Isaiah* — 51, 6.

THE heavens shall vanish away like smoke. A prophetic vision! After something like three thousand
years, the telescope of the astronomer has made it a
reality. The old heavens have indeed vanished. What
would Isaiah say could he come back to learn the manner
of their vanishment?

I shall not attempt to answer that question. But I
wish briefly to summarize some salient aspects of the
contemporary view of the new heavens, in particular to
review in the briefest manner the essential aspects of
new knowledge revealed by contemporary star-gazers
and their associate workers, and to interpret the bear-
ings of the new revelations on questions of cosmology
and cosmogony.

Never was there greater activity in the field of astronomy than in our generation. Never before were so
many men engaged in the investigation of one aspect or
another of the multifarious problems that confront the
watcher of the skies. Were we to attempt merely to
glance into all these fields, the result would be confusion
rather than clarification. We must be content to select
a few salient aspects, not, perhaps, because they have
greater importance than other aspects, but because they
bear more directly upon the larger problems of the
origin and destiny of the universe.

Stated otherwise, problems that concern the evolution of the celestial mechanism; the origin of the world-system; the sequence of changes signalizing the life-history of a star.

In particular we must ask whether the astronomer of our day is prepared to write a new story of the creation of the universe in lieu of the abandoned one, and to make a new forecast as to the future history of the universe in general and the solar system in particular.

At the outset, let it be recalled that only a few things at most that could in any proper sense be called new and original are achieved in any single generation.

The seemingly new ideas and discoveries that gain prominence in any age are, almost without exception—as the history of science reveals—merely old ideas revived, rejuvenated, and forced into view of a generation whose predecessors had refused to receive them.

Thus it was that even the revolutionary conception of Copernicus had been anticipated by Aristarchus in the old Greek days; the nebular hypothesis of Laplace was but a mathematical elaboration of the unaccepted nebular hypothesis of Kant, who had also amazing prevision of a theory of the slowing of the earth's rotation by tidal influence which has only been revived in our own day.

The newest conception of the spiral nebulæ as "island universes" far beyond our galactic system, but restates the case as it was put forward by the elder Herschel, who in turn borrowed it from Kant (the same immortal philosopher already twice mentioned), just as he borrowed his "grindstone theory" of the universe (now again at the fore) from another of his predecessors, Thomas Wright.

It is no disparagement to present-day workers, then,

to say that their tasks are for the most part not new.

On the other hand, it would do less than justice to the work of some of them were we not to recognize that, as words are ordinarily used, their contributions are essentially original.

For example, the classic work of Langley and Abbot on solar radiation, carried out with that necromantic instrument, the bolometer; the spectacular achievements of Campbell and Boss and Kapteyn in the observation and interpretation of the movements of stars; the laborious and brilliant work of Pickering and his successor Shapley and their associates in the spectroscopic survey of the heavens; the weirdly penetrating scrutiny of the sun by Hale; and the exploration of the depths of space with giant telescopes by the associates at Mt. Wilson; the dazzling measurement of the diameter of a star by the interferometer of Michelson; the paradoxical interpretation of the universe by Einstein; and the penetrative cosmogonic speculations of Chamberlin and Moulton, of Hertzsprung and Russell, of Sir James Jeans, and of Prof. A. S. Eddington.

Of course the contemporary astronomer has for the most part ceased to be a "star-gazer" in the literal sense of the word.

He uses telescopes, to be sure, but he has the aid of artificial eyes, in the form of spectroscope, spectroheliograph, and photographic plates.

There was a time when the maker of star-charts gazed hour after hour through the tube of his meridian circle, and made his record by pushing a button when an individual star crossed the line of the spider web that bisected his field of vision.

Now a few photographic plates exposed in succession record the positions, more accurately than the unaided

THE GREAT NEBULA IN ORION

eye could possibly do, of more stars than any individual worker could observe with accuracy in a lifetime.

Then there are modern tricks of technique that give opportunity for comparisons of star positions until recently undreamed of.

Thus the campaigner who goes in quest of records of a planetoid or of Mars for parallax purposes, makes two exposures on the same plate, at intervals of a few hours, slightly shifting the position of the plate in order that the stars may not be exactly superimposed, and subsequently makes his observations in the laboratory by meticulous measurement of the planet's changed relations to the stars in its neighborhood.

Again a plate may be exposed, for minutes or hours, in the focus of a great telescope directed toward the infinite hosts of stars; then removed from the telescope and stored away undeveloped, to remain for perhaps ten years before it is taken out and again adjusted for observation of the same field. After this second exposure, the plate is developed, and the double images of thousands of stars, lying side by side, will show the patient laboratory searcher whether individual stars or groups of stars have shifted their positions anomalously, thus revealing "proper motion."

What would Halley, who first detected the "proper motion" of three stars through study of ancient and contemporary charts, have thought of this? What would Herschel have thought, who detected the line of flight of our own solar system through study of the proper motions of the half-dozen stars whose records were available?

Need we wonder that the contemporary star-searchers, with such mechanical aids, have been able to detect the lines of movement of thousands of stars, and thereby to gain at least a general impression as to the aggregate movement of clusters, groups, and even gigantic streams of the migrating hosts of our galaxy?

It was thus that Prof. Lewis Boss, of Albany, learned the secret of about forty stars in the constellation Taurus, between the Pleiades and Aldebaran that are moving through space together in parallel lines at uniform speed, like a flock of birds.

It was thus that Jacob Cornelius Kapteyn, the Dutch astronomer, discerned that vast numbers of stars of our galaxy are moving in two great streams, almost in opposite directions, seemingly bound for goals beyond our universe. It was Kapteyn, indeed, who first suggested the method of observation by double exposure of a photographic plate.

After he announced his discovery, in 1904, the conception of the stellar universe as a chaos of stars, each with its own independent motion in space (as Prof. W. M. Smart has phrased it) was effectively disposed of. The conception that the chief mass of stars of our galaxy is revolving about a uniform center, like the structure of a spiral nebula, was however, rendered doubtful. At all events, it was made clear that there are great groups of stars that do not partake of such a motion.

In recording the movements of the stars, the photographic plate, adjusted merely in the focus of the telescope, has obvious limitations. It can tell us nothing as to line-of-sight movement.

But here the spectroscope takes up the story. In the service of various workers, notably Prof. W. W. Campbell, of Lick Observatory (later President of the University of California), it yielded amazing records of the movements of a multitude of stars. The lines of the spectrum

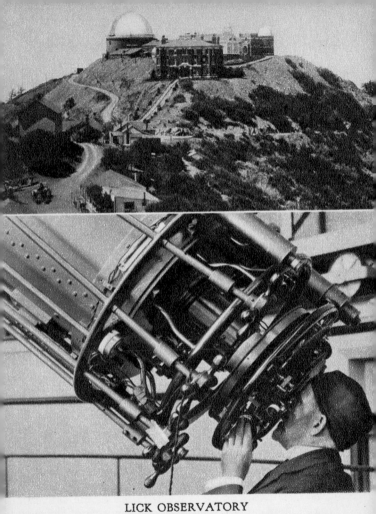

LICK OBSERVATORY

PROFESSOR ASAPH HALL USING THE GREAT
EQUATORIAL TELESCOPE

are shifted toward the violet if a star is approaching, toward the red if it is receding (the so-called Doppler effect). Records thus secured supplement the cross-flight records of the ordinary negative.

Taken together, they have gone far toward revealing the structure of the stellar universe.

What would old Hipparchus and Ptolemy have said could they have witnessed the stars of their outermost fixed sphere of the heavens hurtling hither and yon? What would the Arabian star-gazers and their European successors to the time of Tycho have thought, could they have seen the glassy sphere in which they conceived the stars to be imbedded, shattered into myriad fragments by the mad rush of stars by millions upon millions (where they conceived the total number in existence to be but a few thousands), dashing at an average speed of perhaps twenty miles per second—some of them ten, twenty, perhaps even a hundred or a thousand times that?

Verily, the old heavens have vanished, even as Isaiah predicted—tho the new heavens are perhaps not precisely the firmament that his prophetic eye envisaged.

Let us survey with the contemporary astronomers some salient aspects of the new heavens.

II
PERFECTING THE SOLAR YARDSTICK

IN THE year 1900 various bands of astronomers, equipped with a score or so of photographic telescopes, set out on what was whimsically dubbed the Eros Campaign. Being interpreted, this means that the astronomical bodies of the world went gunning for an inoffensive planetoid named Eros.

Planetoids, it will be recalled, are very small members of the sun's family, which circulate, like a shower of meteorites, in the otherwise vacant space between the orbits of Mars and Jupiter. It will be recalled, further, that the first of these little planets to be discovered was found, by chance, on the first day of the nineteenth century, and that thereafter the discovery of planetoids was the avocation of many astronomers in odd hours.

After the use of the photographic plate made detection of the planetoids relatively easy (these bodies making a dash on the plate which reveals stars as dots), so many planetoids were in evidence that for the most part astronomers no longer bothered to give them names, but were content to number them.

When the number reached the thousand mark, exception was made, for sentimental reasons, and the next three planetoids discovered were very appropriately christened Piazzia, Gaussia and Olbersia in commemoration of the three distinguished astronomers associated with the first discoveries of minor planets — the Italian observer, Piazzi, who saw the first planetoid; the German mathematician, Gauss, who gave the formula that

enabled astronomers to find it again after it was lost; and
the physician-astronomer Olbers, who made the second
planetoidal discovery.

The quest of planetoids continuing, and a few astronomers rather specializing in this field, the number of
little bodies observed has increased so rapidly that it is
hard to keep track of the statistics, the 1930 census being
of the order of two thousand.

It is interesting to note that one member of the family,
discovered by a Viennese observer in 1928, was given the
name Hooveria, in honor of the American Food Com-
missioner who had endeared himself to Europe, and who
subsequently became President of the United States.

It will further be recalled that the discovery of the
first planetoid, christened Ceres, deprived the old seven-
day myth of its significance, by giving an eighth planet
to the solar system. In due course, the discovery of
Neptune, of the major series, followed; and, as we have
just seen, the name of the minor planets soon was legion.

Our present concern with them is not with the group
of two thousand, but with a single member, the one
named Eros.

This little body, discovered in the year 1898, stands
out among all the rest for the sole reason that its exceedingly elliptical orbit brings it, on occasion, nearer to the
earth than any other planetary body ever approaches.
And thereby hangs the tale I wish to tell. It concerns the
highly important matter of the accurate survey of the
entire solar system.

It is through studies of Eros, made during the "campaign" to which I have referred, that the most recent and
most accurate estimate of solar-system distances has been
made. Before we inquire just how this was accomplished,
let us for the moment envisage the conditions of astro-

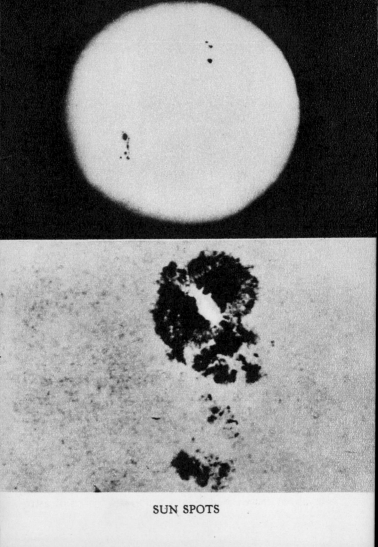

SUN SPOTS

nomical measurement as applied to the sun and its neighbors.

The yardstick of the solar system is a line joining the center of the earth and the center of the sun.

To be slightly more accurate, it is the *average* distance of the earth from the sun—for of course the actual distance varies with each sector of the elliptical orbit— being greatest at aphelion (summer solstice) and least at the opposite end of the circuit. At the periods of the equinoxes, the distance is intermediate.

The unit distance for solar measurements is the calculated mean distance—what would be the radius if the earth's orbit were circular.

The convenience of such a yardstick for measurement of the distances of the planets is obvious.

It is rather odd that, after more than two hundred years of testing, there should still be doubt in the minds of astronomers as to the exact length of this yardstick itself. In particular this seems odd, when we reflect that there are at least a dozen methods of measuring the yardstick, and that concerted efforts have been made from time to time by the astronomers of the world to make the measurements accurate.

The explanation, however, is merely that astronomers are accustomed to demand extreme accuracy in their measurements of all types. There has been no question at all for several generations as to the approximate length of the earth-to-sun yardstick. The distance has long been known to be *about* 92,870,000 miles. The question at issue concerned only the odd thousands of miles by which the length of the yardstick departs from the round number.

It was to test this refinement of measurement that the "Eros Campaign" of 1900 was undertaken.

As already intimated, the offensive weapon in this campaign was the camera. The object of the campaigners was to photograph from different points of view the region of the heavens in which Eros appears at the time of its nearest approach to the earth. Eighteen photographic outfits, variously located, were devoted to this purpose. A large number of highly satisfactory photographs were taken.

What then? Well, now comes the strangest part of the story. These photographs, individually and collectively, to casual inspection reveal nothing of the slightest significance.

They are simply ordinary-seeming star-charts, consisting of the usual black background dotted with points of light.

Of course one of these points of light, in each photograph, is the image of the little planet Eros. But that, tho of course an essential feature of the photograph, tells nothing to the casual inspector. The work of measuring the yardstick had only just begun when the photographs were completed, the plates developed, and the entire series placed in the hands of Mr. A. R. Hinks, of the Cambridge Observatory, who was to be responsible for the "coordination and discussion" of the Eros observation.

His task was to sit down with those negatives and measure them, and make calculations from his measurements, day after day, week after week — and in the aggregate year after year.

As to the measurements, it is recorded that on the Cambridge plates the displacement of images is of the order of one-twentieth of an inch. The mathematical calculations involved are much longer — best measurable in terms of months.

MOUNT WILSON OBSERVATORY. DOME OF THE
100-INCH HOOKER REFLECTOR

If astronomical workers were given to a popular type of illustration, we might learn how many times round the globe the formulæ used by Mr. Hinks in solving the Eros puzzle would reach if laid end to end.

A gruesome task, the average layman would think it. But for a mathematical astronomer, a task fraught with allurement. Probably it was with a sigh more of regret than of relief that Mr. Hinks finally brought his calculations to an end, and was able to announce that the "angle subtended at the sun by the earth's radius is 8.807 seconds of arc."

This "fundamental angle" is called the solar parallax. It represents the angle of the lines from the ends of the earth's radius meeting at the center of the sun.

As the length of the earth's radius, which thus makes the third side of a triangle, is definitely known, it is a relatively simple problem in triangulation to translate the parallax into terms of distance in miles between the earth and the sun — which is the yardstick we are all along seeking.

This distance was found to be, in round numbers, 92,900,000 miles.

As already explained the distance in question is the average or mean distance.

This newest measurement does not conspicuously change the estimate hitherto accepted, based on multitudes of measurements by different methods — including, prominently, observation of the transit of Venus across the face of the sun, calculations from observation of the occultation of the moons of Jupiter, observations of Mars (in particular by Gill in 1877), heliometer observations of the minor planets Victoria and Sappho: calculations based on the "Constant of Aberration" of light, studies of the parallactic inequality of the moon, and spectroscopic measurement of the earth's orbital speed.

The distance 92,876,000 miles, resulting from a study of the constant of aberration, was held by Young to be on the whole perhaps the most accurate measurement available a generation ago; this being the equivalent of the parallax 8.803.

It will be seen that the newest measurement varies from this by only 4-thousandths of a second of arc.

The Paris conference of 1911 adopted 149,450,000 kilometers (92,870,000 miles) as the most likely value for the mean distance in question. Mitchell and Abbot, writing in 1927, give 92,870,000 miles as the generally accepted value — a parallax of 8.80.

Inasmuch as Newcomb as long ago as 1896 adopted 8.797, plus or minus 0.007 seconds, as the value of the solar parallax to be used in the planetary tables, while Harkness in 1891, at a discussion of many measurements, adopted as the final value 8.809 seconds, plus or minus 0.006, it will be seen that the newest measurements, based on study of the images of little Eros, do not differ significantly from the earlier estimates.

There was, indeed, a divergence of only a small fraction of a second between nine groups of estimates collated by Newcomb, in which the measurements of nineteenth-century astronomers were recorded.

We may feel fairly confident, then, that if an airplane capable of achieving an average speed of one thousand miles an hour were to set out for the sun, it would have an average journey ahead of 92,870 hours.

It must be recalled, however, that on January 1st, the earth is about 3,000,000 miles nearer the sun than on July 1st.

At first blush, that would seem to suggest that the

voyager would do well to plan his journey for the winter season, but when we reflect that, even at a speed of a thousand miles an hour, almost twelve years would be required to reach the goal, the time of starting seems less important.

A concluding word as to why this measurement has all along been considered so vitally important. The reason is almost adequately implied in the characterization of the mean solar distance as a "yardstick." But to get its full significance, one must understand that the measuring unit can be applied to all members of the planetary family in a very curious way.

It may be recalled that Kepler's third law establishes a certain relation between the orbits and distances of all members of the planetary family. This made it possible to establish the relative locations of the planets — to draw a true chart, to scale, of the entire planetary system as then known — before any actual measurement has been accurately established.

It follows that when any particular interval of the scale could be determined in miles, all other distances were at once revealed, as it were automatically.

It is precisely the case of an ordinary terrestrial map, say of the United States, in which the boundaries of the States are accurately drawn, so that relative sizes are revealed at a glance, or more accurately by measurement, but where there is no clue to the actual size of any State, unless (as is usual) down at the corner of the map a "scale" is given which supplies the interpretation.

Similarly with the chart of the solar system. When you know the distance between the earth and sun, all other distances may be at once measured.

SUN PROMINENCES 80,000 MILES HIGH

ANOTHER SOLAR PROMINENCE

III

THE NEW SUN

AWAY back in the year 1857, the Gold Medal of the Royal Astronomical Society of England was awarded to a middle-aged apothecary of Dessau, Germany. The name of the recipient was Samuel Heinrich Schwabe. The work for which he was honored was the study of sun-spots.

It appeared that the apothecary had early developed a penchant for observing these blemishes on the face of our luminary, the discovery of which by the first users of telescopes two centuries earlier had so disturbed the equanimity of the Aristotelians of the period. Aristotle, it will be recalled, had conceived the sun as a perfect body; assuredly unmarked by blemishes of any type. His doctrine accorded with the ecclesiastical conception of the perfection of all heavenly bodies.

How great was the shock to all lovers of tradition when the perfect body was seen to be pock-marked, can be fully appreciated in our iconoclastic generation only by active use of the imagination.

But horror gave way in due course to indifference, and for a good many generations no one paid any particular attention to the spots on the sun, beyond noting casually that they were sometimes more and sometimes less abundant — appearing and disappearing without seeming rime or reason—and that by observing them one could discern that the sun revolves on its axis in a period of about twenty-six days.

THE MOON THROUGH THE BIG REFLECTOR

About the middle of the nineteenth century, however, it was discovered by Lamont, of the Munich Observatory, that there is a periodicity in the phenomena of earth magnetism, and that the fluctuations are singularly in accord with fluctuations in the number of sun-spots.

The fact that the earth's magnetic pole is not at the geographical pole had long been known; also that there are daily fluctuations in the exact direction of the needle's pointing. Lamont's discovery was that these fluctuations increase and decrease with fair regularity in a period practically identical with the sun-spot period.

In the following year, 1852, it was pointed out independently by three observers that the maximum deviation of the magnetic needle occurred in periods of greatest sun-spot abundance.

Such association between a seeming defect in the sun's constitution and a curious anomaly of one of the least understood phenomena of our planet, naturally excited general interest in the scientific world. Then it was, and apparently not before, that scientists in general began to inquire just who was responsible for the knowledge of periodicity of the sun's spots.

The answer brought to the front the apothecary of Dessau, whose queer avocation hitherto had been, it appeared, its own reward. Now, at the hands of the Royal Astronomical Society the zeal of this amateur was to receive more tangible recognition.

In presenting the medal, the president of the Society pronounced this well-merited encomium:

"Twelve years hath Schwabe spent to satisfy himself —six more years to satisfy, and still thirteen more to convince, mankind. For thirty years never has the sun exhibited his disk above the horizon of Dessau without being confronted by Schwabe's imperturbable telescope, and that appears to have happened on an average of about three hundred days per year. This is, I believe, an instance of devoted persistence unsurpassed in the annals of astronomy. The energy of one man has revealed a phenomenon that had eluded even the suspicion of astronomers for two hundred years."

Once more the amateur in astronomy had triumphed —as Horrox and Bradley and Herschel and Olbers had triumphed.

In particular, one recalls Horrox, the devoted young clergyman, because he also achieved fame by observation of the sun—even of a spot on the sun, tho in this case the spot was not a local blemish, but merely the silhouette of the planet Venus shadowed against and creeping across the face of the great fire-ball.

There the comparison ends, for the English clergyman had made his observation in a brief term of hours of one day; whereas the apothecary of Dessau required for his discovery a long term of years. The English amateur died at the age of twenty-two; the German amateur had attained the age of sixty-eight before his labor of love, then of more than thirty years' duration, gained recognition.

Schwabe's observations revealed maximum groups of sun-spots at intervals of about ten years. Subsequent investigations, in which reports of earlier observers are included, give an average period of slightly over eleven years. There is, however, a considerable variation. Periods of maximum spots sometimes are two years ahead of schedule.

It developed, also, that there is a typical and curious distribution of the spots, inasmuch as they are seldom seen within five degrees of the solar equator, nor in latitudes higher than thirty-five north or south. The be

THE SPECTROHELIOGRAPH FOR MAKING STUDY
OF THE SUN'S SURFACE

ginning of a new cycle after a time of freedom from spots, shows an eruption in or near latitude thirty-five, according to the researches of Carrington, whence, year by year, they invade lower latitudes, like a spreading eruption on the face of a measles-patient.

Observation of the movement of spots at different latitudes appeared to show that the sun rotates in about twenty-five days, but that the fluid character of its constitution permits the spots at higher latitude to lag behind, accomplishing their circuit of the sun in a period of about twenty-seven and one-half days.

These tangibilities were known, while the nature of the spots remained an entire mystery. Further knowledge was not forthcoming until a new instrument called the spectroheliograph was available. The basic idea involved occurred independently about the year 1890 to Dr. G. A. Hale, whose work at Mt. Wilson was to make him famous, and to the French astronomer Deslandes.

This instrument invented by Dr. Hale, adjusted to a telescope, performs feats of wizardry in the interpretation of the sun's surface, spots included, which were quite unpredictable.

The spectroheliograph travels across a plate, receiving light only through a narrow slit. In effect it photographs the light of a single line of the spectrum. The result is a picture in no way resembling anything that could be produced by the ordinary exposure of a photographic plate.

Among the most surprizing discoveries made by Dr. Hale in the course of his varied studies of the sun's surface was that sun-spots are fields of localized magnetic influence.

It had for a good while been believed that sun-spots represent virtual craters in the sun's substance, due to

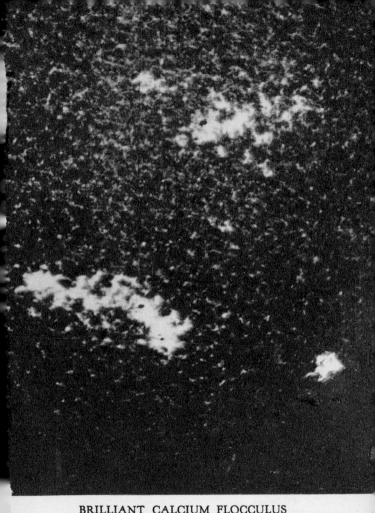

BRILLIANT CALCIUM FLOCCULUS
SURROUNDING THE SUN

localized explosions of extravagant dimensions. The spectroheliograph confirmed this idea, and added the highly interesting information that the uprushing vapors take on a whirling motion, and may therefore be likened to cyclones in the earth's atmosphere.

It was observed that those cyclones occurring in the sun's northern hemisphere usually have a clockwise rotation; those in the southern hemisphere having anti-clockwise rotation; thus corresponding with the normal direction of cyclonic air currents on the earth. There are, however, exceptions to the rule.

In the study of these solar cyclones, Professor Hale was led to notice a spectrum effect which seemed to him to suggest that the light coming from the sun-spots shows the influence of electrical and magnetic forces.

Specifically, what was noted was that the lines of the spectrum seemed to manifest the Zeeman effect.

This is a phenomenon that derives its name from having been first observed and described by Professor Zeeman of Amsterdam in 1896. His observations had nothing to do with the sun, but were made in the labora-tory with the aid of an ordinary flame and a powerful electromagnet.

The essence of his observation was this: When an incandescent substance is placed in the field of an electromagnet, each of the lines representing that sub-stance in the spectrum is split into two or more lines.

If the rays of the light which produce the spectrum are parallel to the lines of force of the magnetic field, spectrum lines are divided into two lines, each of the new lines consisting of light that is said to be circularly polarized.

If, however, the rays of light producing the spectrum are transverse to the lines of magnetic force, the spectrum line is divided into three lines, the central one occupying the original position, and the lateral ones being plane polarized.

Hale, studying his sun-spots, confirmed his early impression that the Zeeman effect is exhibited in the solar cyclones. The spots are, then, centers of magnetic influence. Presently it was found that the spots exist in pairs, one representing the positive and the other the negative pole of a magnet — such pairs usually being located at greater or less intervals, side by side, parallel to the sun's equator.

In 1925, Hale and Nicholson announced the discovery that the sun's spots of a new eleven-and-a-half year cycle, which appear in high latitudes after a minimum of solar activity, are of opposite polarities in the northern and southern hemispheres.

"As the cycle progresses the mean latitude of the spots in each hemisphere steadily decreases, but their polarity remains unchanged. The high-latitude spots of the next 11.5-year cycle, which begin to develop more than a year before the last low-latitude spots of the preceding cycle have ceased to appear, are of opposite magnetic polarity."

This law of reversed polarity in successive cycles was found to hold in all but 41 cases out of a total of 1735 bipolar groups. It was therefore concluded that the full spot period, at least that referring to magnetic polarity, is 23 years and not half that time, as the study of spot frequency had seemed to prove.

Professor Turner of Oxford, from a different standpoint, has also found evidence for a difference between successive periods of spot frequency, pointing to the double period.

"We may therefore ultimately find," says Professor

THE SUN ECLIPSED BY THE MOON
THE MOMENT OF TOTAL ECLIPSE

Fath, "that the true spot period, as to both magnetic polarity and frequency, has a mean duration of 23 years."

The observed magnetic condition of the sun's spots makes it seem less anomalous that so-called magnetic storms, associated with violent deflections of the compass-needle, may occur on the earth during periods of sun-spot activity. The terrestrial phenomena, which include the induction of strong electric currents in telegraph and telephone wires, may be explained tentatively as due to the bombardment of the atmosphere by electrons driven out from the sun on sunbeams.

Electronic bombardment of the atmosphere may perhaps also explain the interesting phenomena of the aurora borealis.

Meantime the new studies of sun-spots, much as they reveal, leave the causation of the spots themselves as much a mystery as ever. Why they appear seldom more than 40 degrees from the equator, and chiefly in the belts on either side of the equator between 10 and 30 degrees of latitude, is quite unknown. And as to why they show the curious periodicity which the Dessau apothecary discovered so long ago, there has never been even a plausible hypothesis.

Leaving the spots with their curious vortex motion out of consideration, the remainder of the sun's surface, as recorded by the spectroheliograph, rather curiously suggests an airplane picture of the top of a uniform layer of clouds.

In reality, the resemblance is something more than accidental. The instrument, because it receives the thin film of light of a particular wave-length, takes cognizance of the presence of only a single elementary substance in a given sweep across the surface of the sun.

THE 100-INCH REFLECTOR. DOTTED LINES SHOW
SIZE OF THE FUTURE 200-INCH REFLECTOR

In one view, for example, it shows the layer of hydrogen, which lies far out in the chromosphere, at the surface of the sun.

Another picture may go a little deeper and show a helium surface.

Yet another reveals a cloud-like stratum of calcium, even higher in the sun's atmosphere than hydrogen.

The presence of the calcium in a gaseous or super-gaseous condition at this high level, is a surprize. It can be explained only on the assumption that the calcium atoms, under solar conditions, are partially disrupted, and are swept out into space by the radiation pressure which rushes out in all directions from the great central furnace.

It is estimated by Professor Eddington that the temperature of the surface of the sun is about 6000 degrees Centigrade; and that the temperature rises as the solar depths are reached, to something like 40,000,000 degrees Centigrade at the center. Such figures are little more than words, so far as clear comprehension of such unworldly conditions is concerned; but they serve at least to give us the impression of an amazing caldron which is as much hotter than a ball of white-hot iron as such a ball is hotter than a cake of ice.

We are all familiar with heat as a mode of molecular motion; but the degree of heat here predicated must be due not to the mere jostling of molecules and atoms of matter against one another, but to the actual disruption of the atoms themselves.

In the modern view, the atom, as originally conceived by Lord Rutherford, and more elaborately envisaged by Niels Bohr, is a miniature planetary structure, with a central mass of protons (in part mated with the electrons, except in the case of the hydrogen atom) and

outlying planetary electrons, revolving at relatively remote distances in orbits which, under normal conditions,
are as definitely fixed as the orbits of the sun's planetary
families.

The orbital electrons may be driven out of their
course through impact with other similar or dissimilar
atomic systems — such impact as is involved in the
collision between the molecules of a gas.

If the collision be not too severe, the electrons drop
back to their normal orbits in due course, and in so doing
give out the equivalent of the energy which they received through impact.

The energy thus given out, determined as to precise
character by the distance from which the electron falls
back to its orbit, or the particular orbit into which it
falls, goes out as "radiation energy."

In the older view, this manifested itself as waves in
the ether. The newest view does not altogether discard
the waves, but is emphatic in declaring that the energy-
discharge is not a continuous stream, but goes forth in
what might be thought of as successive arrows or bullets,
each of which is called a quantum.

Such is a very crude statement of one essential of the
"quantum theory" of Planck, which has taken the
modern physical world quite by storm. And such is the
Rutherford-Bohr atom, depicted also in only the most
general terms, which equally took the world by storm
toward the close of the second decade of our century,
but which before the close of the third decade had begun
to be challenged as to some of its salient characteristics.

For the moment at least, however, the picture of the
planetary atom, with almost its entire mass in the central
proton-sun, and with its electron-planets, each bearing
a unit quantity of negative electricity, remains as a

clearly envisaged structure of exceeding convenience for the theorist who would explain the bewildering phenomena (among others) of the sun's internal structure and unbelievable output of energy.

So when we speak of a temperature of 40,000,000 degrees, we must contemplate not merely the interaction of atoms, as such, but the actual disruption of atomic systems.

This conception would have been considered heretical to the point of scientific nihilism in the generation preceding our own. For the conception involves not merely the severing of orbital electrons from their central suns but, in one manner or another, the actual destruction of at least a portion of the veritable substance of the atom — a violation of the sometime "axiom," that matter is indestructible.

In another sense, the matter is not annihilated, but only transformed into energy.

There are two opposite ways, it is conceived, in which this may possibly take place.

It may be that under conditions of incredible pressure, through which the atomic systems are stripped of their orbital electrons, until protons and electrons become an inchoate mass instead of a collection of orderly mechanisms, there is opportunity (say when the conditions of pressure change as the inchoate matter-stuff boils up toward the surface of the sun) for the coming together, in pairs, of protons and electrons to form hydrogen atoms, and the subsequent coalition of these primordial atoms in groups of four, to form helium atoms.

It is believed that this is the initial process that somewhere, sometime, has taken place in the universe in the building up of matter.

All the more complex forms of matter, of the entire

POURING A LADLE OF WHITE-HOT GLASS IN
MAKING THE GREATEST TELESCOPE EYE
———
EXAMINING THE 20-TON TELESCOPE DISC

THE 200-INCH LENS HEATED ELECTRICALLY, TO
PREVENT TOO RAPID COOLING

THE LARGEST SOLID PIECE OF GLASS EVER CAST

series of ninety-two elements, may be considered as built of helium atoms with residual hydrogen atoms (never more than three of the latter for any given element) to fill in the chinks, as it were, in case the new element is not one that can be made of helium blocks without remainder.

If this does not take place, then the release of an enormous fund of energy is accounted for.

For it is known that the helium atom, tho made up of four protons and four electrons, is not precisely four times as heavy as the hydrogen atom, which comprises a single proton and a single electron. That is to say, there has been loss of actual mass — primordial matter — in the construction of a helium atom out of four hydrogen atoms.

There seems no alternative to the belief that this matter has been transformed into energy.

Mathematical calculations give assurance (on the basis of one of Einstein's formulæ) that the amount of energy thus released is colossal.

It is estimated, for example, that the amount of hydrogen in a teaspoonful of water, if thus made to combine to form helium, would release enough energy to drive the largest of ocean liners across the Atlantic.

Here, then, we have a possible source of energy-release that might go far to account for such conditions as appear to obtain in the depths of the sun.

According to another view, however, the interior of the sun is the very last place in the world where such combination of protons and electrons, to build up larger atoms, could be expected to take place.

This other view looks rather to the depths of interstellar space as the location where the marriage of protons and electrons, to form helium and perhaps other elements in sequence, is more likely to take place. The "cosmic ray" of Professor Millikan may conceivably represent the flow of energy from such a creative mingling of the primordial elements out in space.

This, obviously, would have nothing to do with the question of temperatures at the heart of the sun.

There remains, however, the alternative thesis, according to which the disrupted atoms, already predicated at the heart of the sun, make possible, not indeed the creative marriage of protons and electrons, but the dashing together of these elements to their mutual destruction.

Such annihilative unions would, it may be supposed, take place in the very depths, at the region of greatest pressure and most intolerable crowding.

It is estimated that the crowding together of protons, stripped of their outlying electronic orbits, may be so great, under conditions of pressure at the center of some stars, that a cubic inch of the primordial matter there may have the mass — scientific equivalent for weight — of a ton of matter as we know it at the earth's surface.

Under these conditions, it does not seem to strain the probabilities — holding to the modern view of the interchangeability of matter and energy — to suppose that coalition between proton and proton or between electron and proton may result in the actual dissipation of these primordial substances.

And if this takes place, the output of energy would be not merely of the order of that which attends the building of a helium atom, but many times greater, because the entire bulk, and not merely a small fraction of the proton is transformed into energy.

In the view of such mathematical astronomers as

THE COUNTING OF TIME BY THE MAYAS.

Introducing Glyph

9 Bactuns of 400 years each

10 Katuns of 20 years each

10 Tuns or years

10 Uinals or months

0 Kins or days

Falling on the day 8 Ahau 3 Chen.

The four upper Glyphs correspond to the first four panels in the illustration on the left. The lower glyph appears on the bottom panel of the Stela.

THE WESTERN STELA.
Moving the awnings describing the passing of time.

Western Stela silhouetted against the setting sun

Ruined Maya city of Copan

The direct distance between the two Stelae is 4.8 miles

Monolith erected to commemorate...

Copan River

Base of Eastern Stela. From this point the priest took observations for correcting their time tablets

Top portion of Eastern Stela broken off

Eastern hill top

CORRECTING THE RECKONINGS BY MOVING THE WESTERN STELA WHEN THE MOVEABLE NEW YEAR'S DAY FELL ON THE SAME DAY AS THE COMMENCEMENT OF THE AGRICULTURAL YEAR.

At a later date the Stela was moved more to the north. The sun then set behind this point when September 6 and April 9...

Dates inscribed on the Stela

Position of the Stela when the sun sets directly behind it on September 6 and April 5.

Stone base block.

DIAGRAMMATIC VIEW OF THE POSITION OF THE STELAE.

Summer solstice 21st June

April 9 — Western Stela

Sept 2nd — Equinox 21st March 23rd September

Copan

Eastern Stela

Winter solstice 21st December

A MAYA SUNDIAL

Professor Eddington (original sponsor of the theory, in 1924) and Sir James Jeans, such a transformation of matter into energy is incessantly taking place within the structure of the sun and the other suns that make up the stellar universe.

These daring theorists speak as freely of the reduction of the mass of the sun through such transformations as if they were dealing with a structure that could be weighed from hour to hour and its loss of mass evaluated on the scales.

Jeans estimates even, in specific terms, by how much the sun is being reduced in mass day by day, and tells us no less specifically the distance by which the earth's remoteness from the sun must be increased under mandate of the law of gravitation, in compensation (about 40 inches a century).

Meantime Eddington gives us an inkling of the radiation-power of the energy released by such (imagined) transformation of matter, in the picture he gives of what takes place in the sun's chromosphere.

This outer layer of the sun's atmosphere consists, he says, of a few selective elements which are able to float — not on the top of the sun's atmosphere, but on the *sunbeams*.

"The art of riding a sunbeam is evidently rather difficult, because only a few of the elements have the necessary skill. The most expert is calcium. The light and nimble hydrogen atom is fairly good at it, but the ponderous calcium atom does it best."

Eddington goes on to explain that the layer of calcium suspended on the sunlight is at least five thousand miles thick.

The skill of the calcium atom in thus riding sunbeams is explained as due to its capacity to lose an electron

ANCIENT CHINESE ASTRONOMICAL
INSTRUMENTS

under impact of the escaping energy, and then to seize it back again.

It must be able "to toss up an electron twenty thousand times a second without ever making the fatal blunder of dropping it. That is not easy even for an atom. Calcium (as it occurs in the chromosphere) scores because it possesses a possible orbit of excitation only a little way above the normal orbit, so that it can juggle the electrons between these two orbits without serious risk. The average time occupied by each performance is one 20,000th of a second."

That does not seem a long time, yet it is divided into two periods, according to theory.

During one period the atom is patiently waiting for a light wave to run into it and throw out the electron.

During the second period the electron revolves steadily in the higher orbit before deciding to come down again. Professor Milne is credited with calculating the relative lengths of these two periods. "Milne's result is," says Professor Eddington, "that an electron tossed into the higher orbits remains there for an average time of a hundred-millionth of a second before it spontaneously drops back again. I may add that during this brief time it makes something like a billion revolutions on the upper orbit."

Which may seem difficult — but not for an electron.

Such, then, are the conditions believed to obtain in that flat flocculent cloud of calcium which the spectroheliograph reveals and depicts on the photographic plate, as making up a chief constituent of the sun's outermost atmosphere.

Of course the energy which thus plays with calcium atoms, as a hurricane plays with autumn leaves (with the difference that the atoms manage to settle back into

A REFRACTING TELESCOPE

eddies and thus are not blown altogether away) passes on into space in every direction.

The infinitesimal modicum of it that is intercepted by the earth constitutes the heat and light without which there would be no life on our planet.

Such is the newest answer to the problem of the sun's heat, which remote generations did not so much as propound, since to them it seemed natural enough that any observed phenomenon might go on forever; but which puzzled sorely our predecessors of the latter part of the nineteenth century.

The doctrine of Helmholtz, exposited by Kelvin, that the sun's heat is due (solely) to contraction, is as obsolete as the older conception that it is merely a ball of fire, being consumed like so much coal.

The newer doctrine that the sun's energy may be due to the presence of radio-active elements was, perhaps, the parent of the doctrine of transmutation from matter to energy, just outlined, tho the parent thesis is so far outstripped as to seem almost old-fashioned, notwithstanding its recent origin.

IV
NEW LIGHT ON THE STARS

IT REQUIRES no instrumental aid to prove that the sun sends us light and heat. But very little was known about the precise quantities of energy involved and in particular about the variations in quantity from hour to hour and from day to day, until Professor S. P. Langley invented the instrument called the bolometer.

Langley is known to the astronomical world for his pioneer work in charting the sun's rays with this instrument. His popular fame was chiefly gained by his experiments in the attempt to develop a heavier-than-air machine that would fly.

In the day when the air as yet was unconquered, Langley made a model that did fly, and he came bitterly near success with his man-carrying "aerodrome," which dropped into the Potomac only a few days before the Wright Brothers achieved success and immortal fame down at Kitty Hawk.

It will be recalled, perhaps, that the Langley machine was subsequently taken from its repose in the Smithsonian Institution and made to fly — but only with the addition of the equivalent of the warping wings which the Wright brothers had developed and without which no aeroplane takes the air even to this day. But Langley was as near success as anyone was destined to come before the two young men solved the riddle, and his ultimate failure, when the goal seemed so near, was a bitter experience.

In that day, the philosophy that imbues the mind of the star-gazer must have been a solace. And fortunately for himself Langley was endowed with an abiding sense of humor and an imagination that would enable him to evaluate the significance of his failure — and thereby to make the disappointment endurable.

The bolometer with which Langley made his extraordinary measurements of the sun's varying output of energy, is described by Dr. C. G. Abbot, who has followed up the work no less searchingly, as an electrical thermometer, with two hair-like ribbons of platinum, as long as one's fingernail, blackened with lampblack, one of them fitting behind a metal plate.

"As the rays of the solar spectrum fall upon the exposed one, it warms it above the temperature of its hidden neighbor. The tiny temperature difference, even if less than 1/1,000,000 degree, suffices to alter the electric current balance of which the two ribbons form parts, and a little mirror, smaller than a pinhead, is turned by the electro-magnetic impulses which the current-change produces.

"A tiny shaft of sunlight reflected by the mirror moves across a photographic plate, and so records the warming or cooling of the exposed ribbon of the bolometer."

There is a clockwork mechanism and a photographic plate, and the solar spectrum is moved back and forth across the sensitive wires, making a permanent record of what Langley called "solar-energy spectrum curve" or "bolograph."

This record showed not only the energy of the spectrum itself, but also recorded heat far beyond the ends of the spectrum visible to the eye. The method thus measures the total energy of the solar radiation, not merely that associated with the visible rays.

THE MILKY WAY

The same apparatus, and a somewhat similar one called a radiometer, has been used to test also the energy of the stars.

So sensitive was an instrument used by Nichols and Hull, that it had power to evaluate an amount of energy equivalent to that which would be received from a candle twenty miles distant.

It could perform the necromantic task of registering and measuring the heat from larger stars and planets. Radiant heat is, after all, only a longer-wave form of light, but we are so accustomed to think of starlight as "cold" that the idea of its inherent warmth seems anomalous.

High interest attaches to such energy-tests as these, but of course the chief star-records, upon which our knowledge of the sidereal universe depends, are exclusively light-records. In recent years, however, various highly ingenious methods have been devised for interpreting the light-messages in terms of the structure of the almost infinitely distant light-emitting stellar body.

To begin with, of course the spectroscopic record tells much, when it has revealed the chemical composition of a star, even in part.

In our nearby star, the sun, for example, no fewer than sixty-six of the terrestrial elements have been located.

The rays of the stars proper, enfeebled by distance, do not give so comprehensive a record.

Yet there are thousands of stars in which nearly as familiar elements are unequivocally revealed as if the tests were being made in a laboratory. On the other hand, with perhaps a single exception, there is no spectroscopic record of any solar or stellar element that is not known here on the earth.

In general, the chemistry of the stars is familiar terrestrial chemistry.

It will be recalled that helium was discovered in the sun (and indeed so named because of its location there) long before it was known as a terrestrial element — tho now we know that it is present everywhere in the atmosphere in minute quantities, and is a relatively abundant exudate in certain oil wells; and, indeed, a universal by-product of radioactive elements everywhere in the soil.

In some stars, the spectrum of helium is so conspicuous that the name "helium stars" seems appropriate.

Other stars are known as "hydrogen stars" because their outer atmosphere, possibly also their deeper structure, is aglow with that element.

Iron is widely distributed in others, and the less familiar element titanium is more conspicuous than might be expected — tho the general lack of familiarity with this element is due not to its scarcity in the earth's crust, but to the fact that hitherto no conspicuous commercial use has been found for it.

We have seen, in the preceding chapter, that the modern view takes cognizance of the probability that the more complex elements are dissociated under the conditions of heat and pressure that obtain in the sun.

Since the stars are only distant suns, vast numbers of them enormously larger than our own luminary, it goes without saying that similar conditions must obtain in their depths.

It is easily conceivable that "hydrogen stars" may consist almost or quite exclusively of the element hydrogen alone, since that is the most primitive of all elements — the basic structure out of which the more complex elements are believed to be built.

In any event, it is known that many of the largest and most brilliant stars are of excessively tenuous structure — some of them composed of gas of such extreme rarefaction that it is the equivalent of what in the terrestrial laboratory is called a high vacuum.

This seems almost incredible, since we are accustomed to think of stars as solid bodies.

But the conclusion is unescapable, when the observed bulk of the star is considered in connection with its mass, as demonstrated by a neighboring star with which it constitutes a binary system.

The bulk of a star, it should be explained, is not determined by actual measurements (except in the few recent cases where the magic interferometer of Michelson has been applied), but is inferred from the star's brightness in connection with the parallax, or more usually lack of parallax, that demonstrates its extreme distance.

It may be added that the stars which have yielded directly to measurement with the interferometer — Betelgeuse, Aldebaran — show diameters closely corresponding to the estimates that had previously been made by the light-gaging method.

The fact that the stars vary in color from blue or white to orange or red early led to suggestions for their classification on this basis. In this work Father Secchi, at Rome, was the pioneer. But as he depended upon visual observation, he necessarily only prepared the way for the more elaborate investigations that were subsequently to be made with the spectroscope.

At Harvard Observatory, under the directorship of E. C. Pickering, this work was developed on the basis of roughly a quarter of a million stellar structures, photographed with an objective prism instrument. The re-

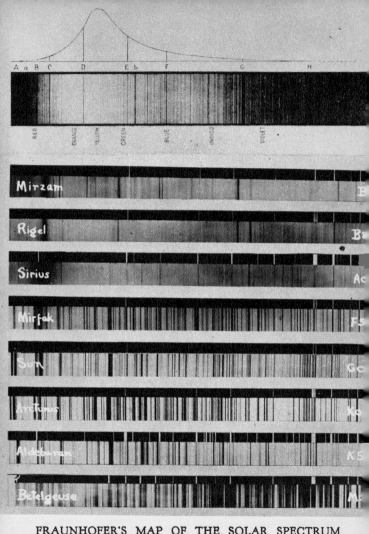

FRAUNHOFER'S MAP OF THE SOLAR SPECTRUM

TYPICAL STAR SPECTRA

sults of this work, collated notably by Miss Cannon, have been published in nine large volumes, dedicated as a memorial to Dr. Henry Draper, a great pioneer in stellar spectroscopy.

According to this so-called Draper Classification, the principal classes of stars are denoted in the following order, by the letters O, B, A, F, G, K, M, R, N and S.

Ninety per cent of the stars are included within the six classes B to M. Each type of star has subdivisions, numbered from 1 to 9, except type M, the subdivisions of which are lettered.

Class B stars show prominently the lines of hydrogen and helium. In some of these stars, the helium is partially disrupted; such also is the state of silicon, oxygen, and nitrogen. Stars of this class are sometimes called "helium stars" or "Orion stars." Prominent representatives are Rigel, Regulus, the bright stars in the Pleiades, and several stars in the constellation of Orion.

The stars of the remaining prominent classes are characterized as follows by Dr. W. M. Smart:

"Class A. In spectra of this type, the lines of hydrogen are the most prominent. The lines of several metals, notably those of ionized calcium and magnesium, are in evidence, but weak in comparison with the conspicuous lines of hydrogen. Sirius, Vega, and Castor are stars belonging to this class.

"Class F. In spectra of this class, the hydrogen lines become less prominent and the lines of metals — notably the H and K lines of ionized calcium — gain in importance. Near the end of this class, at F8 and F9, the spectra bear a strong resemblance to the solar spectrum. Typical F stars are Procyon and Canopus, which are white stars.

"Class G. This is the class to which the sun belongs. The spectrum is remarkable for the enormous number of

metallic lines — notably the lines of neutral, that is, un-
ionized iron; the lines of hydrogen and ionized calcium
are still prominent. Typical stars are the sun and Capella
— both of type G; these stars are yellow in color.

"Class K. Bright stars in this class are Arcturus and
Aldebaran. The lines of ionized metals become weaker;
the lines of neutral metals become stronger. Near the
end of this class there is evidence of the bands of titanium
oxid. The stars of this group are orange in color.

"Class M. The important feature of stars of Class M
is the great strength of the bands of titanium oxid; the
lines of neutral metals are also prominent. The stars in
this class are red; Antares and Betelgeuse belong to
Class M.

"The spectra of the sequence B to M, are, with a few
exceptions, absorption spectra — that is, each spectrum
consists of the rainbow colors, red, orange, etc., to violet,
crossed by dark lines. In Class O the most important lines
are *bright* lines of hydrogen, of ionized helium, carbon,
oxygen and nitrogen; there are, in addition, several
bright lines of unknown origin. The classes R, N and S
may be regarded in some respects as subdivisions of
Secchi's Class IV — they are red stars and comparatively
rare in the heavens."

It will be noted that there is here a gradation from
blue stars to red.

It is justifiably inferred that the colors evidence variations in temperature, comparable to those shown by a
heated iron which becomes first red-hot and then white-
hot.

Elaborate analyses of the spectroscopic records of these
stars, supplemented by Dr. Abbot's tests with the bolometer, have led to interpretations of technical character —
"Wien's law," "Stephan's law," "Planck curves" — of

the typical temperatures of the various types of stars under consideration, according to which stars of the white or blue type exhibit a surface temperature of upward of 35,000 degrees Centigrade, while stars of the M or red type may have as low a temperature as 3,000 degrees — comparable to the temperature of molten iron.

Well may it be spoken of as "indeed a marvelous achievement that the temperature of stars, tens and hundreds of light years away from us, can be measured with such remarkable precision."

Here, it is observed, the astronomer comes to the aid of his confrère, the physicist, since in the hottest stars, matter exists under conditions unapproached in the laboratory, and the study of stellar spectra leads to a more intimate knowledge of the structure and behavior of the atom than could be attained from merely terrestrial observation.

It is these studies, chiefly, that have made the conception of the partly dissociated atom — the nucleus wholly or partly stripped of its electrons — familiar.

In the myriads of sidereal laboratories open to our observation, through the medium of the necromantic spectroscope and telescope, we witness transmutations of elements comparable to those which the medieval alchemists perennially dreamed of, and which the nineteenth-century chemistry mistakenly pronounced an inconceivability.

One would search long for a stranger dénouement than that of the efforts of the searchers who turned their eyes upward to the far places of the heavens.

There remains an exceedingly curious additional fact to be noted in connection with the stars of the Draper classification.

It is found that, by and large, the hot stars are moving

with relative slowness and the red stars with greatly increased speed, there being an even gradation throughout the intermediate ranks.

Thus the average for B stars, according to Dr. Plaskett, is 6.5 kilometers per second; that for Class A stars 10.9 kilometers, and so on, up the scale to a speed of 17.1 kilometers per second for the cool, or red, stars of Class M.

There is ample food for reflection in this record of disparity of speed between stars of different types. The thought naturally suggests itself that, conceivably, the hotter, more gaseous, star may be younger, and therefore has not yet acquired the momentum which the cooler stars have attained through falling for a longer period toward some imaginable center of gravity represented by the center of the universe itself or by some aggregation of matter which has dominating influence.

There is at least a certain measure of plausibility in such a suggestion.

But have we any evidence that the blue stars are indeed younger than the red ones?

In examining that question, we are brought face to face with the question of the origin of the stars and their life-history.

There is no other astronomical question, perhaps no question in any other field of science, that has greater interest than this. Let us make inquiry as to the way in which contemporary astronomers have endeavored to answer it.

In so doing we shall find ourselves at the very frontiers of twentieth-century astronomy.

As we pass from the theme of cosmology to that of cosmogony, we shall witness the effort to read the story of Creation, the story of the birth of heavenly bodies,

THE CROSSLEY REFLECTING TELESCOPE,
LICK OBSERVATORY

the story of the evolution of world-systems, with the scroll of the firmament itself for our text.

Which after all is only putting ourselves in the attitude of our remote ancestors of prehistoric times, and of their descendants of the early civilizations, who perennially scrutinized the heavens, and whose interpretations were recorded by the scribes at the very dawn of history, to become traditions, sacred with age, which we of this latter day are only now beginning to challenge effectively, and supplant.

But there is this significant difference, that we of the new generation have instrumental aid in searching out the meaning of the sidereal scroll, which our forebears were denied. Perhaps we may hope, then, that the new interpretation will be an advance upon the old one. Let us in any event inspect it.

The basic classification of stars, everywhere accepted in the early part of our century, is the "Draper Classification" above outlined.

As originally interpreted, the series represents consecutive stages of star-development — presumably from a hot stage through successive stages of cooling, to be followed by extinction.

But about the year 1913, two men, Professor E. Hertzsprung, of Leyden, and Professor H. N. Russell, of Princeton University, independently made observations that tended to render this interpretation debatable.

They observed that stars of the M (cool) type of the Draper classification are of two quite different orders of magnitude — one group enormously large, the other group amazingly small, as stars go.

The two groups came to be dubbed, respectively, Giants and Dwarfs — these "happily descriptive terms" being chosen by Hertzsprung.

It was Russell who followed up the discovery in the year 1913 by collecting data for all the known members of the two groups, between two and three hundred, whose distances were then approximately known. He calculated their absolute magnitude — that is to say, the magnitude each star would have if fixed at such a distance from the earth that the parallax would be one-tenth of a second.

Dividing the stars into their spectrum classes, he produced an extraordinary diagram which showed, among other things, that in Classes B and A (hot, white or blue stars) there are no *faint* stars; and in Classes K and M (cool, red or iron stars) there are no stars of *medium* brightness; all are either very bright or very faint.

A veritable bombshell this — a stick of dynamite cast into the world of astronomical speculation. For it had come to be taken for granted that stars of one Draper class are stars of one age. Young stars, large and white-hot; old stars, small and only red-hot, which is the equivalent of cool, as things go in the sidereal world.

And now it appeared that a cool red star could be either a giant or a dwarf — at once young and old, according to the standard interpretation.

It was altogether disconcerting.

But Professor Russell's observations were fortified by an unexpected wealth of new material, resulting from the discovery of a method of testing star parallaxes with the spectroscope, as applied by Dr. W. S. Adams, of the Mt. Wilson Observatory.

Now there could be no question that the red stars are divisible into two groups of totally different magnitude.

One group of the red stars (M) was found to be ten magnitudes, or ten thousand times, brighter than the other group.

The average giant appeared to have a million times the volume of the average dwarf.

And there were no intermediate red stars between the giants and the dwarfs. That, indeed, was the strangest part of the story.

The interpretation of the anomaly, as given by Professor Russell, was that red giants and red dwarfs represent the youth-stage and senility-stage respectively of a star, and that the intermediate stages of the star's life-history are represented by the other coteries — B, A, F, G and K of the Draper classification with their various subdivisions — which had hitherto been supposed to belong to independent categories.

The life-story of a star, according to this new interpretation, begins with a vast, relatively cool nebulous stage represented by the giant M; evolves through Class G and the other intermediate stages to a culmination in the white or blue star stage of Class B, or perhaps O; after which there is the decline of advancing age, with decreasing size, progressive cooling; a second childhood in a Class G stage (our sun is here); and ultimate senility in the cool dwarf of the final Class M.

This is such a progress of evolution and devolution as Lockyer had conceived and clearly outlined a good many years before.

But since most astronomers had paid no attention whatsoever to Lockyer's speculations, or had put them aside as utterly visionary, the new estimate of the life-history of a star, fortified now by a wealth of concrete observations, came as a bewildering surprise.

Needless to say, the new speculations were not universally accepted. But in the ensuing years additional evidence in their support was found in the results of investigations of independent character.

THE 69-INCH REFLECTOR AT PERKINS
OBSERVATORY

There is, for example, the altogether amazing feat — the most spectacular astronomical achievement of the century — of measuring directly the diameter of a star.

This was accomplished at Mt. Wilson, with the great reflector, equipped with the extraordinary instrument called an Interferometer, the creation of Professor A. A. Michelson, of the University of Chicago.

The actual measurements were made largely by Dr. Pease.

The instrument consists of a long beam of structural steel, placed across the upper end of the tube of the one-hundred-inch telescope. This beam carries near either end a small mirror, and the two mirrors can be adjusted by sliding back and forth, until their reflected beams from the image of a star are brought together in such wise as to produce alternate bright and dark bands, or "fringes."

With a certain separation of the two light-collectors, the fringes almost disappear.

Here the position of the two mirrors is measured, and by a calculation which, from the standpoint of the mathematician, is not unduly intricate (but which no non-mathematical mind could be expected to understand), the diameter of the star from which the light-beams came, is determined.

As a matter of course the stars first selected for measurement were certain ones accredited to be of gigantic size — brilliant, not because of their relative nearness (as in the case of Sirius), but because of their actual magnitude.

The first of all was the famous Betelgeuse, known from antiquity as the famous red star of first magnitude in the shoulder of Orion, and bearing in recent times a name which it received from the Arabian astronomers.

This big red star (a dullish red to naked-eye view) was accredited one of the largest of the company of Class M giants.

The interferometer measurement, made on a night of December, 1920, brilliantly confirmed the estimate of the enormous size of Betelgeuse. The measurement of the star was an almost unbelievable achievement (recall that even this giant appears only as a point of light in the field of the most powerful telescope).

The implication of the measurement — showing that the theoretical estimates of star dimensions were dependable — was, from the standpoint of cosmogonic speculation, tremendously significant.

Mere words and figures give no conception as to the magnitude of this Class M giant. To say that Betelgeuse is 250,000,000 miles in diameter is to use meaningless words.

To say that it is 300 times the diameter of the sun perhaps makes the picture a trifle more concrete.

Best of all, perhaps, is the estimate which shows that if Betelgeuse were placed in the position of our sun, its surface would extend far out to the neighborhood of the orbit of Mars, leaving the earth encompassed within the substance of the great M star itself, at a depth of more than 30,000,000 miles.

Appropriate indeed for such a colossus — yet after all how inadequate — is the name Giant.

Other measurements followed. Mira Ceti proved even larger than Betelgeuse — big enough to extend far beyond the orbit of Mars were it in the position of our sun.

Aldebaran, a yellow star, proved of intermediate size. The brilliant white star Sirius, and Vega, both of Class A, are enormously large in comparison with the sun, to be sure, yet pigmies beside the Class M giants. Indeed,

Vega, much the larger of the two, appears as only a dot, like a period on the printed page, on a diagram that shows Mira something like two inches in diameter.

On this same scale, it may be added, Arcturus appears about the size of a capital O on this page, tho in the sky, to visual observation, this orange star shines at first magnitude.

Only the largest stars can as yet be measured with the interferometer, but the results of these measurements strongly support the validity of estimates made by other methods. And stars of other types form series strongly supporting the Russell theory.

There are certain so-called eclipsing binaries of Class B, for example, whose diameters vary from about three to eight times the diameter of the sun.

This is quite in accordance with theory — since Class B stars are intermediate in age between the red giants and the sun.

Also there is at least one binary of type M that has been under observation.

Estimating the sizes of the components of this revolving system by the usual gravitational methods, it is found that the components of the system are but little more than half the solar diameter. In volume as well as in luminosity they are but insignificant dwarfs.

Their density is about four times that of water — indicating that their structure is of the order of composition of the earth, and vastly more dense than the average substance of the sun.

All this carries out the conception that the giant red stars are in the stage of babyhood, and that the red dwarf stars are nearing the end of their period of luminosity.

So convincing is the evidence that it can be said that

as recently as 1924, the giant-and-dwarf thesis of stellar
life-history seemed by way of general acceptance among
astronomers as the valid interpretation of the evolution
ary history of stars in general.

Nor has the theory by any manner of means been
altogether superseded in the ensuing years.

But it is held by many astronomers that serious doubt
has been cast upon its validity by new discoveries of
another order—the discovery, or interpretation, of the
relation between stellar mass and luminosity.

This discovery or interpretation is associated with the
observation of stars that are called *White* dwarfs — a
type of star not accounted for in the Draper classification, and therefore requiring consideration from another
viewpoint.

The most famous example of the white dwarf clan
(of which only three members all told are known) is
the companion of the bright star Sirius, which was discovered by the American telescope maker, Alvan G.
Clark, after its existence had been predicated theoreti-
cally by the great Bessel because of observed irregularities
in the motion of Sirius itself.

The orbit in which Sirius and its small companion
revolve is accurately known, and the masses of the two
stars. Sirius itself has about two and one-half times the
mass of our sun, whereas the "white dwarf" companion
is smaller than the sun by about one-sixth. Not precisely
a midget, therefore, but a true dwarf, according to
sidereal standards.

As viewed from the earth, the companion is described
as ten magnitudes smaller than Sirius. Otherwise stated,
Sirius is ten thousand times brighter than its companion.

The comparison with the sun, as just made, is mis-
leading.

THE ASTRONOMICAL DRIVING CLOCK

For whereas the mass of the white dwarf is not so far below that of the sun, by the tape line the star is a veritable dwarf, having a diameter of only twenty-four thousand miles — three times the diameter of the earth.

Uranus, the planet next in size above the earth, has a diameter of thirty-two thousand miles. Jupiter, of course, is far larger still.

Thus the companion of Sirius is seen to be a body of ordinary planetary size — yet it is a self-luminous star, shining like any other star because of its own inherent hotness; and shining, indeed, with the spectrum of the F group of the Draper classification, which is just below Class A, to which Sirius itself belongs.

The significance of all this may be summarized in the statement that the density of this white dwarf companion of Sirius is computed to be fifty thousand times that of water.

As Dr. Smart remarks, one ton of the material of this star could be stowed away comfortably in a match-box.

Osmium, the most dense substance known here on the earth, has about twenty-two and one-half times the density of water — as against the fifty thousand of the white dwarf.

It seemed impossible to credit the calculations that ascribed such properties to this star — because ordinary dwarf stars are not white hot, but on the contrary are cool to redness. A way must be found to test the calculation that ascribed such anomalous qualities to the white dwarf.

Enter now the mathematician, Albert Einstein. Not in person, to be sure, but as represented by his world-famed theory of relativity.

The man who applied the theory, in this instance,

was Dr. Adams at Mt. Wilson Observatory. The apparatus with which he worked was a spectroscope. What he did, specifically, was to test the lines in the spectrum of the Companion, and to determine that they are shifted far more toward the red end of the spectrum than could be expected except under one condition.

This condition is that the light sent out from the surface of the white Companion comes from matter of excessive density.

One of the three practical tests suggested for the validity of the Einstein theory is that light from the sun should show its lines shifted very slightly toward the red end of the spectrum, and that light from a more dense body should show them correspondingly farther shifted.

According to theory, if the Companion of Sirius is really as dense as had been estimated, the shift of the lines (technically expressed in terms of kilometers per second, because under other conditions a similar shift represents the speed of a star in the line of sight) should be 20.

Dr. Adams, after making all allowances for motions of the Companion, deduced the value 19.

Obviously, here was something approaching a demonstration. Professor Eddington says of this test:

"Professor Adams has thus killed two birds with one stone. He has carried out a new test of Einstein's general theory of relativity, and he has shown that matter at least two thousand times denser than platinum is not only possible, but actually exists in the stellar universe."

Now for the complication. If the Companion were a cool red star, of low luminosity, it would fall into the scheme of stellar evolution as a dwarf of M type, therefore at the last stage of devolution. But as the case

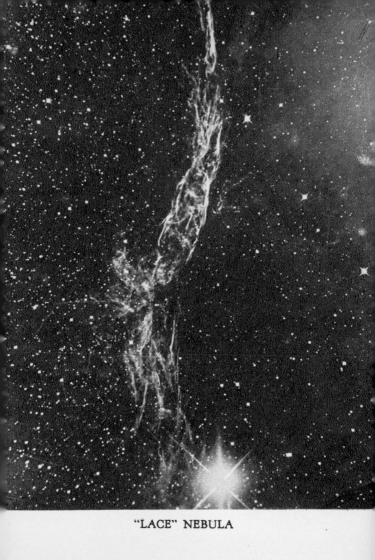

"LACE" NEBULA

stands, the Companion is a brilliantly luminous white star, having the effect of a gaseous structure instead of a liquid or solid, yet being enormously more dense than any terrestrial liquid or solid.

The accepted thesis of the Russell scheme of stellar growth and decay had been that the turning-point in the history of a star at the white stage, came at the stage when a degree of cooling was attained at which the star ceased to be gaseous.

After that, it was supposed to be a matter of continued cooling and contraction, with loss of actual substance, as descent was made to the stage of solid matters, still glowing like red-hot iron, but at a surface temperature not greater than may be achieved in the terrestrial laboratory.

The anomaly of the Companion — and the known presence of at least two other white dwarfs in the stellar system, with the probability that many more exist — was held to vitiate the Russell theory, putting it thoroughly under suspicion.

"We no longer admit," says Eddington, "that stellar substance will cease to behave as a perfect gas at one-quarter the density of water. Our result that the material in the dense dwarf stars is still a perfect gas strikes a fatal blow at this part of the giant and dwarf theory."

He adds, however, that tho the theory of stellar evolution must be considered as in the melting-pot, he is disposed still to believe that the former theory was right in assuming that the sequence of evolution is from diffuse to dense stars.

Yet it appears that, at least as to its broad lines, the theory of stellar evolution presented by Russell can still be maintained if it be conceded that within the body of the star there may take place actual annihilation of matter, or other sub-atomic release of energy, such as was referred to in the preceding chapter when the conditions within the sun were under discussion.

But if this is admitted, there seems no reason why a skeptical attitude should be taken toward the thesis of stellar evolution from cool body to hot body and back again to cool; for the leading mathematical astronomers of today, with certain notable exceptions, have come to accept the possibility of such a transformation of matter into energy, not merely as a working hypothesis, but apparently as a theory firmly believed to be in accord with the actualities.

At all events the Russell theory of the life story of a star stands as the most plausible interpretation of the observed differences in stellar constitutions that has hitherto been presented.

V
STARS THAT ARE DIFFERENT

THERE have been singularly few women to attain prominence in the astronomical world. But at least one woman in our own time has made a major discovery in this field. I refer to Miss Leavitt, and the discovery of the relation between actual brightness and rate of pulsation of the very famous stars known as Cepheid Variables.

The discovery was not made by direct star-gazing. It was made by the more typically modern method of examining photographic negatives in the laboratory.

The negatives under observation were taken at the celebrated Harvard University Observatory at Arequipa, Peru. Their subject was the long-known nebulosity of the southern hemisphere called the lesser Magellanic Cloud — a celestial object invisible from temperate zones of the northern hemisphere, but famed as forming, together with its more conspicuous companion-structure the greater Magellanic Cloud, a unique exhibit in the circumpolar region of the other hemisphere.

These nebulosities were among the phenomena of the southern heavens to which Sir John Herschel gave special attention during his famous sojourn in South Africa.

They have interest, among other things, because they lie far outside the Milky Way as isolated islands of nebulosity, as if two handfuls of the substance of the Milky Way itself had been plucked out and placed near the frontiers of the Galactic system, the two being sep-

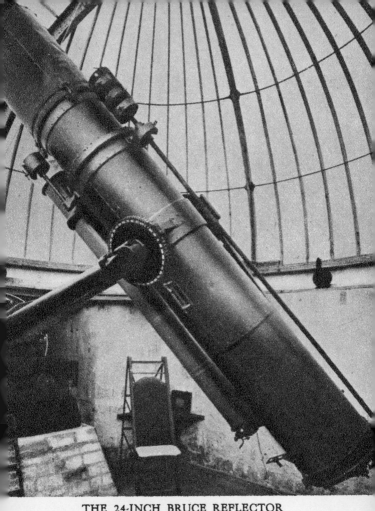

THE 24-INCH BRUCE REFLECTOR
AT AREQUIPA, PERU

arated by about sixty degrees of longitude, but having approximately the same latitude or declination.

Herschel explains that the greater cloud is sufficiently bright to be visible even on a moonlight night, tho the lesser one is then blotted out by the moon's radiance. On a moonless night, the lesser cloud is modestly and the greater one strikingly, conspicuous to naked-eye observation, tho hardly to be called spectacular. To telescopic observation, both clouds are objects of peculiar interest.

The negative that especially attracted Miss Leavitt's attention was taken with the great reflector designed for photographic rather than direct examination of the heavens.

Similar negatives had been many times studied, and very likely this particular negative had passed under many eyes. But it was reserved for this woman observer to note a certain peculiarity of the record which was destined, as subsequently interpreted, to prove of altogether startling significance. Truly momentous, from the standpoint of the science of sidereal astronomy.

Yet the observation in itself was simple enough — albeit demanding keen eyes and a clearly-coordinating brain.

It consisted in comparison of the numerous stars of a certain type among the multitudes of ordinary stars sprinkling the plate — rounding these up, as it were, and checking them off as regards their varying degrees of brightness.

And noting — this constituted the discovery — a certain puzzling relation between brightness of the stars and the unique particularity according to which the stars in question were grouped together.

This particularity was, and is, that the stars in question — the ones sorted out and listed together, tho

sprinkled at various places in the Magellanic cluster—
are *pulsing* stars.

That is to say, they are stars that seem to expand and
contract, with perfect regularity of pulsation, like throb-
bing hearts, each individual star having its own particular rate of pulsation which never varies — the period of
some stars being only a few hours, for others several
days, but in no case more than about a month.

Such pulsing stars would be considered perhaps the
strangest members of the sidereal family were it not that
we ordinarily associate strangeness with rarity, and stars
having this peculiarity can hardly be called rare, as they
are scattered here and there in most parts of the heaven.
On the other hand, in the relative scale — considering
that they number only scores, as against the billions of
stars that do not pulsate — the Cepheid Variables, that
being their name, *are* rarities.

Their strange conduct has naturally excited high
interest since the time, more than a century ago, when
the first member of the clan was observed to manifest its
anomalous particularity of action.

This first of pulsing stars to be observed is faintly
visible to the naked eye in the constellation Cepheus.

Hence the name Cepheid Variable, which came to
stand as the class name for all stars of this type when,
presently, it was observed that the original Delta Cephei
was by no means unique, but had numerous imitators in
various parts of the sidereal system.

As a rule, the Cepheid Variables are located in the
midst of clusters of stars; in particular they frequent
the compact globular clusters — a fortunate penchant
for the astronomer, as we shall see presently.

But what, then, did Miss Leavitt discover as to the
relation between brightness and pulsation-rhythm among

STAR CLUSTER IN THE CONSTELLATION
HERCULES

the Cepheid Variables of the Magellanic Cloud depicted on the Arequipa negative?

Why, simply this: that all the variables of rapid pulsation were *faint* stars — of low visibility. All stars having pulsation-periods of less than one day were exceedingly faint. Stars of progressively slower periods of pulsation were progressively brighter. And the slowest-pulsers of all were the brightest of all.

It should be explained that the pulsation-period — or, to speak more technically, the periods of variation — of all the numerous Cepheids hitherto observed were matters of established record — thanks to the patient observations of the star-gazers of several generations. Miss Leavitt's discovery had nothing to do with that. It was perfectly well known that the numerous Cepheids in the Magellanic Cloud had various periods of pulsation, from very rapid to very slow as things go in the Cepheid-Variable world. The thing that had not been known was that there exists any definable relation between these variant rates of pulsation and the degree of maximum brightness of the different individual members of the clan.

Even now that it was shown that such a relation does exist, nothing much might have been made of it, for offhand it does not seem a matter of particular moment that certain exceedingly faint telescopic stars billions of miles away fluctuate in brightness at short intervals, whereas certain others slightly less faint stars in the same sidereal neighborhood fluctuate somewhat less slowly.

But there were two astronomers in the world who were at once struck, when they heard of Miss Leavitt's discovery, with the thought that here was something that might prove of far wider significance than at first blush appeared — which might, indeed, give the clue

HENRIETTA LEAVITT, WHO STUDIED
CEPHEID VARIABLES

to an altogether new type of investigation of some of the profoundest secrets of the system of stars.

One of these men was Prof. E. Hertzsprung, of Leyden.

The other was Dr. Harlow Shapley, then of Mt. Wilson Observatory, subsequently Professor of Astronomy at Harvard.

To each of them it occurred that Miss Leavitt's discovery that the "period of fluctuation of a Cepheid depends on its candlepower" (as Sir James Jeans phrases it) might be used to test the *distance* of other Cepheid Variables, wherever situated, even to the remotest parts of the visible universe.

The point is this: the Magellanic Cloud is so exceedingly distant from the earth, that the Cepheid Variables scattered through it (tho in reality scattered through an area scores of light-years in extent) may be regarded as practically at the same distance from our planet. Therefore their apparent variations in brightness represent actual or intrinsic variations. The seemingly faint stars are actually of low candle-power; the bright ones of high candle-power.

In a word, a certain rate of pulsation is uniformly associated with a certain degree of intrinsic luminosity.

But special studies had long been made of the apparent brightness of stars; indeed, from ancient times and throughout the generations, relative brightness was the standard according to which stars were listed as of the first magnitude, second magnitude, etc., through the six magnitudes of naked-eye stars and the decreasing magnitudes to the 20th or 21st as revealed by telescopes successively more powerful.

But of course it was familiarly recognized, in modern times, that there is no necessarily close relation between apparent brightness of a star, as we view it, and intrinsic brightness — the matter of distance being an obvious disturbing factor.

The dazzling brilliant Sirius, for example, appears so bright merely because it is relatively near. In the absolute scale it is a star of only moderate luminosity, inferior to multitudes of stars which, because of their distance, are totally invisible to the unaided eye, and appear only as the faintest of specks in the most powerful telescopes.

Astronomers are not altogether without clues for discrimination between apparent brightness and actual brightness, but there had been no star-gage available in the least comparable to the one that the new Cepheid discovery seemed to offer. For here were stars which (thanks to Miss Leavitt's discovery) were now seen to signal directly the record of their intrinsic brightness — to signal it by pulsing at a definite rate, just as a lighthouse beacon signals its identification by its intervals of intermission.

It remained only for the observer to note the *apparent* brightness, as viewed from the earth, of the star whose *actual* brightness was thus signaled in order to compute the relative distance of this star in comparison with the distance of any other Cepheid Variable similarly observed.

Thus one Cepheid Variable could be compared with another as to relative distance throughout the entire group of Cepheids. And if the actual distance of any one Cepheid was known the actual distances of all others could be readily computed.

Thus reasoned the two imaginative astronomers, one in Germany and one in California, on learning of the crude signals that the negative of the Magellanic Cloud had revealed to the Harvard Observatory investigator.

It was the California astronomer, who subsequently became a professor of astronomy at Harvard University, who followed up the clue, and made himself master of a new department of astronomical science—rather, let us say, became the creator of this new branch, as well as its most assiduous cultivator.

No one can think of Cepheid Variables without at once thinking of Prof. Harlow Shapley.

The revelations that have resulted from the use of this new sidereal sounding-line in the hands of Prof. Shapley are nothing less than sensational.

Unimaginable depths of the heavens have been definitely sounded for the first time, by interpretation of the Cepheid-Variable signals. The size, form, and structure of the galactic system and the distances of the globular clusters are gaged as was hitherto impossible, by observation of the pulsing Cepheids.

Prof. Shapley charts the system of globular clusters, and finds that some are 200 light-years away, others more than 200,000 light-years.

Cepheid Variables in the big nebula in the constellation Andromeda locate that famous star-cloud at a distance of not far from 700,000 light-years.

And this is by no means the limit. Sir James Jeans makes quite casually a calculation which starts with mention that Cepheids whose light fluctuates in a period of 40 hours have approximately the luminosity 250 times that of the sun; and goes on to say that a Cepheid Variable of ten-day period, with an apparent magnitude sixteen, from which we receive about as much light as from a candle at a distance of 10,000 miles, is in reality 3,600,000 light-years away.

He adds that the "period-luminosity" law (as the

Cepheïd Variable method is called) "measures the distances of objects up to a million light-years away, with
a smaller percentage of error than is to be expected in
the parallactic measures of stars only a hundred light-
years away."

The "parallactic measures," it will be recalled, are
made by direct observation of a star from opposite sides
of the earth's orbit. Stars 100 light-years away approach
the limit to which this method is applicable.

Such measurements would have comparatively re-
stricted value were they confined to the Cepheïd Variables themselves.

But the value is enormously enhanced because these
variables are usually situated, as already noted, in clusters or in nebulæ, so that the pulsating star signals not
only its own distance, but the distance of thousands or
millions of stars of the localized system in which it is
found. Such groups may be in themselves hundreds of
light-years in diameter, but such dimensions are negligible in contrast with the thousands or millions of
light-years that separate the group as a whole from the
earth—somewhat as one would neglect the difference
beween the near and far side of a football at a distance
of a hundred miles.

The significance of this is made impressive by the
estimate that names 50,000 light-years as the diameter
of the Andromeda nebula. A big football, that!

But while the Cepheïd Variables thus signal distances
across the inconceivable spaces of the universe, revealing
their individual locations, what do the strange signals
tell us of the character of the pulsating stars themselves?

It would be sensational news in the astronomical
world if a definite and conclusive answer could be given
to that question.

For the nature of the Cepheid Variables—the reason for their anomalous fluctuation in luminosity—constitutes one of the outstanding puzzles of Astrophysics, regarding which there has been abundant controversy, with no present prospect of agreement among authorities.

There are variable stars of other types that are no less mysterious. Long-term variables, for example, whose activities do not conform to those of the Cepheids, and regarding which it can scarcely be said that there is a current opinion as to their true character and the meaning of their variability.

Then, too, there are variables known as Novæ, or new stars, which burst out from time to time in the heavens, sometimes attaining the brilliancy of planets, and then fade away in the course of days, weeks, or months. Such new stars have been occasionally observed since the time of Hipparchus.

Tycho Brahe saw one and thought its appearance a miraculous event comparable to the standing still of the sun at command of Joshua or the darkness that came upon the earth at the Crucifixion.

Kepler saw one, too, and so did various of his great astronomical successors. Two notable ones appeared in the early years of the present century.

But nowadays they have ceased to be rarities, under perpetual scrutiny of the heavens with enlarged telescopic eyes. No fewer than eighty have been observed within recent years in the single structure of the great nebula in the constellation Andromeda.

As long ago as 1866, Sir William Huggins, the pioneer worker with the spectroscope, observed a new star, and saw that it had a spectrum of the solar order, with numberless dark lines, out of which shone brilliantly a

TWO VIEWS OF THE LITTLE DIPPER

few very bright lines. There was no doubt that at least two of these lines belonged to hydrogen. The great brilliancy of these lines as compared with the parts of the continued spectrum upon which they fell suggested a temperature for the gas emitting them higher than that of the star's photosphere.

These observations suggested to Huggins that some sudden and vast convulsion had taken place in a star so far cooled down as to give but little light, or even to be crusted over.

"Volcanic forces, perhaps, or the disturbing approach or partial collision of another dark star, had led to the escape of highly heated gases from within; and a chemical combination after the gases had cooled by sudden expansion, gave rise to the outburst of flame at once very brilliant and of very short duration."

Possibly this speculation serves as well as another to explain a phenomenon which confessedly is by no means thoroughly understood.

The great Swedish chemist and cosmologist, Arrhenius, suggested an explanation not altogether dissimilar, to the effect that a dark star plowing into a mass of nebulous matter sets up a conflagration which is temporary, or the effects of which are presently hidden by the great volume of combustion-products, which form in effect a smoke-screen, accounting for the rapid fading away of the star that had blazed up so brilliantly.

The observed fact of the relatively frequent appearance of the new stars in a nebula, as in the case of Andromeda just mentioned, gives a measure of plausibility to the hypothesis of Arrhenius. But we shall require much more light on new stars before an explanation of their phenomena is made that will gain general acceptance.

The great significance of the new stars, in the early day, was to demonstrate to an astonished world that changes can take place in the supposedly immutable structure of the firmament.

Since, in the modern view, the whole universe is in a condition of perpetual flux, this aspect of the matter naturally has no significance.

Another type of variable star, and an exceedingly common type, has its typical representative in the well-known star Algol.

This star, like others of its type, fluctuates in light, waxing and waning at regular intervals, which may vary from hours to days, months, or years.

The variability of Algol itself was discovered by the eighteenth-century astronomer, John Goodricke, in 1782, just at the time when Herschel was beginning to make the stars famous. Goodricke's extended observations established the periodicity of the star as about "two days and nearly twenty and three-fourths hours."

This first observer of a variable star, or rather of the variation of a star, not only established thus its periodicity, but he went on to make tentative explanation of the strange phenomena.

Moreover, he found the correct solution, as was to be demonstrated more than a century later by Prof. H. C. Vogel, an authoritative worker in the field of spectroscopy.

"If it were not perhaps too early to hazard even a conjecture on the cause of this variation," says Goodricke — and then goes on to hazard the conjecture, be it too early or not.

And the conjecture is that the phenomena observed, "could hardly be accounted for otherwise than either by the interposition of a large body revolving around Algol, or some kind of motion of its own, by which part of its body, covered with spots or such like matter, is periodically turned toward the earth."

The first guess was the right one. The variation of Algol is due to the revolution about it of a companion star which, unlike itself, is not luminous. In 1880, prior to Vogel's spectroscopic demonstration, Prof. E. C. Pickering, of Harvard Observatory, made a mathematical treatment of the star's orbit, based on the accurate photometric (light-measuring) observation of the light changes at the time of the eclipse — the particular field of work which Pickering had made peculiarly his own.

The spectroscopic testimony was required, however, to make demonstration complete.

Since it is known that double stars are the rule rather than the exception, it is not strange that variables of this type are exceedingly numerous.

The revolving couple may both be luminous, and yet the light may fluctuate when they are in alinement. Of course the orbit of a binary is only by chance so alined with the earth that eclipse, partial or complete, occurs.

But this happens often enough to make variable stars of the Algol type by far the most abundant of all variables.

It is interesting to note in passing that the same astronomer, John Goodricke, who thus first studied the variability of a star, went on to discover variables of other types, notably the star called Beta Lyræ, a long-term variable whose vagaries are still not well understood, tho shared by a considerable company of other variables of which this is the type; also Delta Cephei, type star of the Cepheids, whose peculiarities claimed our attention a few pages back.

Goodricke died too young to achieve popular fame,

besides being overshadowed by William Herschel. But during his brief life he was a by-no-means insignificant figure in the astronomical world. No doubt the variable stars he introduced to the public had a certain share in developing popular interest, and in particular in spreading broadcast the conception that the "fixed" stars are by no means fixed and invariable.

Herschel himself also studied the double stars, as we have seen, and inferred from their observed occultations their regular swing in orbits explicable on the basis of Newton's law. It was this observation, indeed, that demonstrated the hold of the law of inverse squares on the sidereal bodies, no less than on the bodies of the solar system.

From that day to this double stars have had fascination for a long list of astronomers, including some distinguished amateurs, among them Burnham, the American, who personally discovered no fewer than a thousand doubles while still pursuing astronomy only as an avocation.

In 1906 the Carnegie Institution published Burnham's complete list of all known double stars of the northern hemisphere and to the thirty-first parallel of the southern hemisphere. Data are given for 13,665 stars.

Two stars that are close together may be only optically double, one star being far more distant than the other, and the two having no connection. Physically double stars are those that show a connection either by having a common proper motion or an observed orbital motion beyond their center of mass, the latter being known technically as binary stars.

Aitken and Hussey at the Lick Observatory have made an extraordinary survey of large portions of the northern heavens for double stars. Aitken's book on the binary stars gives the results of the scrutiny of a total of 100,979 stars, for which 5,400 proved to be doubles. Aitken himself had discovered 2,057 of these, and W. Struve 1,053. The conclusion is drawn that about one star in every eighteen as bright as the ninth magnitude in the northern sky is a double star as seen with the 36-inch Lick refractor. The proportion of double stars in or near the Milky Way is slightly greater than at a distance from it.

All this refers to visible doubles.

Reference has already been made to spectroscopic doubles, in binary systems, one member of which may be a dark star.

There is every reason to suppose that numberless stars have dark companions, tho no data are available for a plausible estimate of the proportion of such. Of course the vast preponderance of the millions of stars revealed only by higher powers of the telescope are too faint to record spectrum lines by which their duplicity could be detected.

"Dark star" seems a contradiction of terms. The existence of such bodies in the heavens is an appealing paradox.

Are any of the dark stars afflicted with busy microbes that might be classified as allied to the genus *Homo*? We can only surmise. It would be charitable to hope not.

But if there were such, even the all-seeing eye of the spectroscope could by no chance detect their presence.

The inadequacy of existing instruments to detect the existence of bodies of planetary size and mass, if there are such attendants on stars other than the sun, is emphasized by the observation that the trans-Neptunian planet, Pluto, discovered January 21, 1930, appears as a star of fifteenth or sixteenth magnitude, visible only

THE 24-INCH LOWELL REFRACTOR
FLAGSTAFF, ARIZONA

in the field of the very largest telescopes. Then it appears merely as a speck of light, comparable to many millions of precisely similar specks. (Of fifteenth magnitude stars, the number computed is about 27,500,000; of sixteenth magnitude about 57,100,000.)

Yet the newly-discovered planet, tho by preliminary estimate perhaps four billion miles from the sun, is but a stone's throw away from us in comparison with even the nearer stars. The new planet is perhaps fifty times our distance from the sun. But the nearest stars, Alpha Centauri and its neighbor "Proxima," are at something over 268,000 times the sun's distance.

The light by which Pluto is photographed has come to us in perhaps seven hours. Light from the nearest star takes four and a third years to span the gap between us. And the star-flecks that lie on the plate surrounding the image of the new planet register light that may be scores, hundreds, or even thousands of years from its source.

A trans-Neptunian planet was suspected to exist not long after the discovery of Neptune itself. The calculations of the nineteenth-century astronomers, based on seeming perturbations of the course of Neptune, and on unaccounted-for retardations of certain comets, led to no definite result, but did not dispel the suspicion.

Prominent among the astronomers who were convinced of the existence of a disturbing outer planet, and who made elaborate calculations as to its probable place in the heavens in our epoch, was Percival Lowell, founder of the Lowell Observatory at Flagstaff, Arizona, an enthusiastic amateur of professional accomplishment, popularly known for his elaboration of the theory that the marks on the planet Mars represent areas of vegetation along irrigation canals.

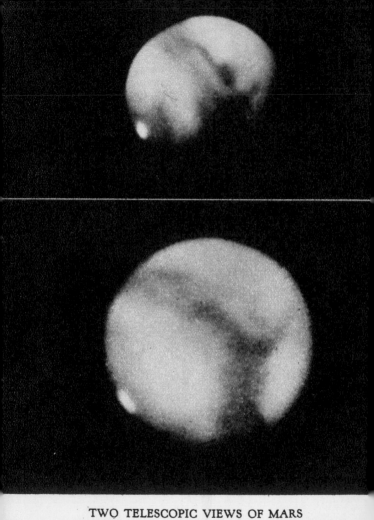

TWO TELESCOPIC VIEWS OF MARS

This theory has not gained general acceptance, but the name of its chief proponent is assured perpetuity by the discovery, at the Flagstaff Observatory, fourteen years after its founder's death, of the trans-Neptunian planet, in the region where his calculations had located it.

The discovery was the result of specific search, made with a telescope especially designed for the work of photographing smaller stars. The light-speck representing the planet was first seen (close to the position of Delta Geminorum, a few degrees from Pollux) by a young photographer, Clyde W. Tombaugh, on a negative taken January 21st, and reported at once to the director of the observatory, Dr. V. M. Slipher. He and his associates confirmed the discovery, but did not make it public till several weeks later. Partly to make assurance doubly sure, partly perhaps for sentimental reasons, they withheld the announcement till March 13th, which is the anniversary of Herschel's discovery of Uranus (1781) and also of the birth of Percival Lowell (1855), whose life-work the discovery in effect laureated.

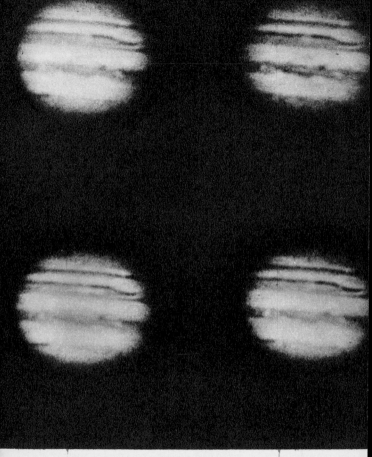

JUPITER PHOTOGRAPHED AT THE LOWELL
OBSERVATORY

VI

STAR NUMBERS AND DISTANCES

INTERPRETED by the Leavitt-Shapley "period-luminosity law," the Cepheids in nebulæ appear to confirm the preconception that many of these, including all the spiral nebulæ, are so remote that they may be thought of as "island universes," even as Kant and Herschel in the old days regarded them.

We shall see before we are through that there is perhaps another possible interpretation. But the conception of the spiral nebulæ as island universes, or independent universes, outside our own universe, the galactic system, is the orthodox view of the astronomy of our epoch.

This view has been fortified not alone by Professor Shapley's studies of the Cepheid Variables, but also by another series of altogether remarkable observations, made in particular by Dr. W. S. Adams, of Mt. Wilson Observatory, in which the wizardry of the spectroscope has been put to a new and strikingly successful test.

Briefly, this amazing instrument, which hitherto had revealed the chemical composition of the stars and tested their line-of-sight movement, was to reveal also the parallax — that is to say the distance — of thousands of stars vastly too far away to be tested by the method of triangulation.

The method is based on the fact that when spectroscopic study was made of the lines in spectra of the stars of known distance, it was found that in stars of the same type — giants and dwarfs of Class M in particular —

spectral lines that were faint in one were intense in the other. The numerical difference could be interpreted in terms of difference of absolute luminosity of the surface from which the light emanated.

In other words, here was a method of testing the absolute or actual luminosity of any star that could be spectroscopically photographed. And, as we have seen in connection with the Cepheid Variables, if actual luminosity can be known, a comparison with the observed apparent luminosity gives data for calculation as to the distance of the star under observation.

In the annals of the astronomer, it is found convenient to state star-distances from the earth in terms of parallax. But of course parallax can always be translated into terms of light-years or of miles — tho the last would involve the use of interminable rows of figures or of such meaningless phrases as "trillions of trillions."

The point of the moment is that this new method of spectroscopic parallax-determination reveals the distances of coteries of ordinary stars, just as the Cepheid Variable method revealed the distance of stars with which these anomalous bodies are associated.

Obviously the two methods could be used to check each other on occasion. It appears that their findings are, generally speaking, in accord.

The general result is that the astronomical world has become accustomed to the contemplation of sidereal distances which, were it not that they are altogether incomprehensible, would be utterly staggering.

A third method, which associates absolute luminosity with mass, assuming that, surface for surface, stars of the same spectro type are of the same degree of brightness (a basic principle in Prof. Russell's celebrated scheme of stellar evolution) has supplemented the other methods. In a word, the attack on the problem of star-size and star-distance has concentrated from many directions, and the new knowledge as to details of the celestial mechanism is bewildering in its profusion.

The technical character of most of these investigations makes it necessary for the layman to take their findings quite on trust, but confidence that the new estimates are by no means chimerical was justified by the results of the direct measurement of the diameters of several of the largest stars — which were surprizingly in accord with dimensions predicated by the earlier estimates.

The direct measurement in question, made at Mt. Wilson by Dr. Pease with Prof. Michelson's wonderful interferometer, has been spoken of as the most notable achievement in practical astronomy of the present century.

But the method can be applied only to a few of the very largest stars that are relatively near, and after all its results are only corroborative — tho in that enormously important — of the more comprehensive results of the application of the principle of period-luminosity in connection with Dr. Shapley's puzzling variables, the principle of spectroscopic parallax as applied by Dr. Adams, and the interpretation of Prof. Russell's principle of the relation between mass and luminosity among stars of the same spectroscopic type.

Spectroscope and photographic plate are still the chief accessories of astronomical equipment, as they were a generation ago.

But new methods of application, and new interpretations, have so extended their field of usefulness as to change the entire complexion of contemporary astronomical research. It cannot be said that the new interpretation of the heavens involved is revolutionary.

Rather it is as if a powerful searchlight had been made to play on the old celestial mechanism, enabling the astronomer of our day to peer into its recesses with clear vision, where before there had been at best a twilight view or the fog of inadequately supported speculation.

The sidereal system as thus envisaged estimates the stars of our galactic system — the structure of which the Milky Way is the backbone — as numbering, probably, from 100 to 300 billion.

The former estimate is that of Professor Shapley, the latter that of Professor Eddington.

Such figures being totally without meaning for any mind, it makes no difference which may be nearer the truth; or whether some more modest estimates should be substituted.

Suffice it that the number of stars in our galaxy is inconceivably great.

No one doubts nowadays that all these stars are in motion, tho the movements of only a few thousand have been accurately charted.

Of course our sun moves along with the rest, and the direction of its flight—carrying the planetary system with it—has been accurately charted by noting the direction of apparent movement of the nearer stars which appear to shift backward in comparison with more distant stars, just as telegraph poles from a car window shift back against the distant landscape.

Another method of testing the sun's flight is spectroscopic. By noting the apparent speed of approach of a given star at different periods of the year, a difference may be observed (in case of a star properly located) which may be interpreted as movement of the observer through space. Of course, account must be taken of the known movements of the earth, rotational and orbital.

THE GREAT NEBULA IN ANDROMEDA

But a residual movement may remain which is to be interpreted as flight through space of the entire solar system.

The so-called apex of the sun's flight, as determined by these various tests, is located toward the bright star Vega—which will one day be the pole star.

The most accurate designation of this apex of the sun's flight is held to be that made by Lewis Boss, based on investigation of the proper motions of more than 5,000 stars.

The exact position, as he determined it, is given as Right Ascension 18 hours 2 minutes; Declination, plus 34.3 degrees.

A slight departure as to the declination is shown by the investigations of Campbell and Moore of the Lick Observatory on the radial velocities of more than 2,100 stars. In one part of the sky the stars on the whole are approaching, in the opposite part they are receding, while in the region between, they are, on the average, doing neither. They find the point toward which the sun is moving to be Right Ascension 18 hours 2 minutes, in agreement with Boss, but Declination 29.2 degrees— a difference of 5 degrees, or 10 apparent diameters of the moon.

It is of interest to recall that the newest estimate of the direction of flight of our sun with its attendant planets varies by only a very small angle from the direction estimated more than a hundred years ago by Herschel—whose inspired guess had foundation in observation of only seven stars of observed proper motion, as against the thousands at the service of the modern cosmologist.

Herschel's estimate of the form of the galactic system, and his conception of the nebulæ as island universes lying beyond our system, also find confirmation in the elaborated investigations of the modern astronomer.

When structure of this universe is in question, the nebulæ always come in for a full share of attention.

Nebulæ belong essentially to modern astronomy, since, despite their enormous actual size, they are so distant from the earth or so faintly luminous as to be telescopic objects only, with the single exception, in the northern hemisphere, of the aforementioned great nebula in the constellation Andromeda.

This is faintly visible to sharp eyes as a small patch of light, comparable to numberless nebulosities of the Milky Way—the latter being, in part at any rate, merely groups of more distant stars.

In addition to such apparent nebulosities, there are, of course, numberless actual nebulæ located in the Milky Way, subject only to observation with the telescope, and satisfactorily observable only with telescopes of high power. Indeed, there are two main types of nebulæ and several sub-types, which are found almost exclusively in or near the Milky Way and are therefore known as Galactic Nebulæ.

As classified by Dr. Hubble, these are called planetary nebulæ and diffuse nebulæ.

Of the latter type—the filmy structures familiar in stellar photographs—some are predominantly luminous, others so obscure that they make apparent dark places in the midst of the star pictures; yet others conspicuously mixed, luminosity alternating with obscurity in a way to suggest diffusion of a nebulous structure.

The great nebula in Orion, the Trifid nebula in Sagittarius and the Network nebula in Cygnus are familiar illustrations of diffused Galactic Nebulæ.

Planetary nebulæ are so named because with a telescope of low power they appear to have a small disc, like that of a planet, with a fairly well-defined edge. They are, however, of more intricate form as viewed with higher powers. The so-called ring nebulæ usually have a focus of light, like a bright star, at the center of the target-like ring or bull's-eye within the annulus of nebulous light.

These look more like rings of smoke which some tobacco users puff out than like any other familiar object.

The so-called extra-galactic nebulæ are sometimes of irregular form, but more commonly take the shape of fairly regular ellipses, or else of spirals.

The two types are held to be closely similar in character. Exceptional interest attaches to the spiral form, which is, as we have seen, regarded by some highly competent observers as a world-system in process of evolution.

Both types have well-defined centers of high luminosity, which are, according to one theory, vast aggregations of stars, but which no present telescope can resolve into individual particles of light.

It is highly interesting to note that the prevailing twentieth-century opinion as to the spiral nebulæ is that they lie at enormous distances (even as distances are counted in the sidereal world), and actually beyond the bounds of our galactic system.

That they are, in a word, "island universes," just as Herschel thought them, and as Kant conceived them away back at the middle of the eighteenth century.

The seeming rotation of the spirals, which has been assumed to represent an actual revolution of the component stars and nebulosities of the arms, or indeed of the entire structure, has been verified by the critical observations of Van Maanen, who compared photographs

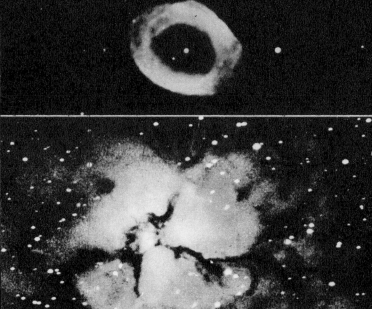

RING NEBULA IN LYRA
———
TRIFID NEBULA IN SAGITTARIUS

taken at Lick and at Mt. Wilson Observatories from ten to seventeen years apart.

He finds in several cases evidence of the change of the positions of small condensations in the nebulæ with respect to stars in the vicinity.

He infers a movement of matter from the nucleus along the arms of the spirals and a rotation of the arms about the nucleus. Dr. Lundmark confirms this. But one observer makes the speed of the shifting masses 16,000 miles per second, the other only 1,500!

The direction of rotation in each instance is not what it looks like to most eyes in the picture, but what the current theory as to the origin of the structure would lead one to expect: the curved arms are swinging with their concave sides forward—as if winding about the nucleus.

Meantime the spectrographic method has been applied in the endeavor to test the rotation of the arms of spiral nebulæ by Slipher, Pease, Wolf, and Wright (I quote here Professor E. A. Fath, of Carleton College) :

Their results show material to be moving away from the nucleus. But they find the velocity to be of the order of only 200 miles per second.

The discrepancy between 200 miles, 1,500 miles and 16,000 suggests that results hitherto attained are only tentative. This is peculiarly apparent when it is added that Drs. Van Maanen and Lundmark (as Professor Smart remarks) made their divergent measurements on the same plates.

Unfortunately the chance to check one method by the other is not quite all that could be wished, because the nebulæ best suited to the spectrographic method, that is to say, those whose planes are inclined at a small angle to the line of sight, are the ones least suited to detect displacement by direct measurements of the photographs. For obvious reasons, those whose planes are most nearly at right angles to the line of sight are best suited to the second method.

About 500 nebulæ of the spiral class have been thus critically observed, ranging in size from the great Andromeda nebula, which is about two degrees in length, or four times the apparent diameter of the moon, to objects so small as to show a definite spiral structure only upon careful examination.

But the large ones on small-scale plates are closely similar to the small ones on large-scale plates.

Apparently size is held to be largely a question of distance.

Prof. Fath, working with plates taken with the sixty-inch reflector of the Mt. Wilson Observatory, illustrates graphically the long-observed tendency of the spiral nebulæ to cluster about the galactic poles—that is to say, the relatively bare spaces of the sky in rectangular relation to the plane of the Milky Way.

He shows further that the clustering is more marked around the northern than around the southern galactic pole; and that the clusters tend to focalize in opposite quadrants of the celestial sphere.

He suggests the possibility, however, that the seeming avoidance of the Milky Way by the spiral clusters may be only an optical effect, due to the obscuration of these distant bodies by the brighter light of the galaxy.

"For the present," he adds, "it seems best to accept the apparent distribution as an observed fact and await further light on the subject."

Prof. Fath, among others, has made somewhat careful estimates of the total number of nebulæ observable in the entire sky.

He states that no attempt has been made by anyone to make a really accurate count, but cites the estimate of several other observers in which the aggregate census varies from 120,000 to more than 1,000,000.

His own opinion is that, for the present, the number of nebulæ within reach of the largest photographic telescopes may be taken provisionally at from one-quarter to one-half million.

No nebula has been clearly shown to have a visual parallax, from which, as from other evidence, it is inferred that nebular distances must in general be measured in terms of thousands or even millions of light-years.

Dr. Hubble, from study of the Cepheid Variables in Andromeda, estimates the distance of that nebula at 700,000 light-years. And this is presumed to be perhaps the nearest member of the family.

If the extra-galactic nebulæ are of the same general order and size and luminosity (a rather hazardous inference, perhaps, but one to which many astronomers are committed), then the smaller of the photographic images represent nebulæ of distances that make the farthest galactic stars seem neighborly.

Dr. Hubble estimates the distance of some of the smallest at 80,000,000 light-years!

He estimates also that with long exposure the one hundred-inch reflector at Mt. Wilson Observatory might record objects at a distance of about 145,000,000 light-years.

Meantime Professor Shapley reports that some of the Harvard plates show a group of nebulæ in the region of Coma-Virgo which may be as much as 100,000,000 light-years distant.

Nothing neighborly about such spiral nebulæ as these!

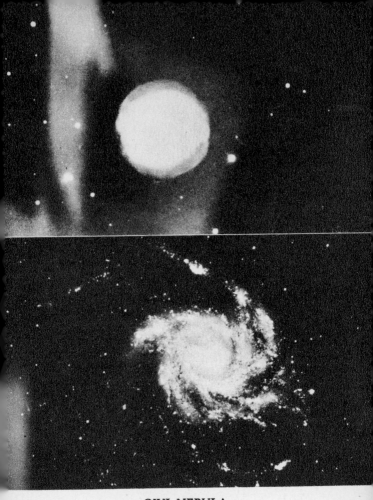

OWL NEBULA

SPIRAL NEBULA

VII

THE STRUCTURE OF THE UNIVERSE

LET us now endeavor to gain an impression of the mechanism of the stellar system, as revealed to, or interpreted by, the modern astronomer.

Let it be said at once that the envisagement of this celestial mechanism does not require us to change very markedly the mental picture derived from contemplation of the grindstone universe of Dr. Wright, exposited at the middle of the eighteenth century, or the allied systems of his contemporaries Lambert and Kant—conceptions that the elder Herschel elaborated and made familiar to the generation that saw the beginning of the nineteenth century.

The familiar figure then suggested—a grindstone—or even better an ordinary watch, may be cited as fairly representative of the shape and form of the galactic system, which is usually referred to as the universe.

The galaxy itself, or Milky Way, represents the plane of the equator of the system, and it seems to form a nebulous coil of stars circling the heavens, chiefly because it represents greater sidereal depths than are viewed in other directions—as if one's position were not far from the center of a watch, and necessarily at a greater distance from the circumference than from the two flattened sides.

As to our precise location in this lens-shaped galaxy, the modern estimates are somewhat different from the estimate of Herschel. He opined that we might be fairly near the center. The modern estimate removes us considerably from that location — being more nearly in agreement in this regard, it may be added, with the estimate of Lambert, who, on the basis of utterly inadequate evidence, made the sagacious speculation that the actual center of the galactic system lies at a remote distance from our sun.

Lambert suggested Orion or Canis Major as the possible center. The modern astronomers do not closely agree with Lambert or with one another, as we shall see. But the modern estimates are confessedly only tentative. No very convincing evidence is available to determine the precise bounds of the galactic system, notwithstanding the agreement as to its general outline.

It is argued that since the Milky Way is practically a great circle in the sky (a "great circle" in the technical sense is a circle whose plane cuts the center of the sphere or spheroid), the sun must lie close to its plane.

The meaning of "close," however, calls for elucidation. According to Gerasimovic and Luyten, as cited by Professor Fath, the sun's distance from the plane of the Milky Way may be estimated at 33 parsecs—about a hundred light-years. Not so very "close," then, in the ordinary acceptance of the word.

But this distance, be it understood, refers to the plane of the Milky Way and not to the center of that plane. The sun's distance from the center is held to be very much more significant. But as to just what the figure should be, authorities are by no means agreed.

We are told that, as regards the location of the center, Kapteyn, guided by his studies of star-drift, favors the region of Cassiopeia, while Shapley, whose Cepheid-Variable and Globular-Cluster studies have made him thoroughly at home in the universe, thinks the Scorpius-

Sagittarius region the more probable one. Yet other astronomers, notably Easton, favor the direction of Cygnus.

Finding here a range of right-ascensions of six hours or so, and a range of declinations covering half a hemisphere, one's mind reverts to the estimate of the sagacious Lambert, and one wonders whether his guess, perhaps, may not be as good as another.

Meantime, one is prepared to learn that the authorities are not well agreed as to the probable distance of the sun from the center of the galactic system—which is no more than might be expected, inasmuch as they so radically disagree as to where that center is.

We are told that Kapteyn has given a provisional estimate of 650 parsecs but that Shapley's work shows rather conclusively that this is too small. His estimate is 16,000 parsecs—a 25-fold increase.

A difference of 50,000 light-years cannot be regarded as quite insignificant, even in charting the universe. But fortunately the discrepancy means nothing so far as actual comprehension is concerned of our relation to the galactic system.

Let it suffice that the authorities are agreed that the sun lies a long way from the geographical center of that system.

A partial explanation of the discrepant estimates of the sun's precise location in the galactic system is to be found in the fact that the study of star movements on a large scale is a comparatively recent development of astronomical science.

The present situation can be understood only if we reflect on our shifting relation to the stars, as regards actual position in space.

One thinks naturally of the shift of position of the

human observer due to the rotation and revolution of the earth. But in the larger view these changes are relatively insignificant. The earth-spin carries the observer round and round in a circle of 4,000 miles radius. The revolution of the earth carries us round the sun in a circle of nearly 93,000,000 miles radius, obviously the widest base line we can use in testing the parallax of a star by the trigonometric method.

But now reflect that the earth, along with the sun, goes forward in a direct line (or conceivably along the arc of an enormous circle) by 367,000,000 miles in a year (about 12 miles per second), and that this shift is added to by a like amount each succeeding year.

If, then, we consider observations made back in the old Alexandrian days by Hipparchus and compare them with observations made in our own time, we have records of the star-maps made from two points of view that differ by 367,000,000 times the number of intervening years. The shift of a single year is the equivalent of almost twice the diameter of the earth's orbit. The seeming backward drift of a star that lies near enough to show parallax must therefore be about twice the amount of the parallax. In ten years, this backward drift, or "proper motion" of the star would be twenty times its parallax; in a hundred years, two hundred times the parallax.

This being clear, we understand why proper motion was discovered long before parallax could be measured, and why the comparison of present-day observation with star-charts, not merely of Hipparchus, but of Bayer, Tycho, Flamsteed, Bradley, and even much more recent observers, gives records of proper motions by thousands.

It is the collation of this almost inexhaustible material that has given the modern cosmologist an otherwise unattainable insight into the movements of the stars.

GREAT REFLECTOR AT THE PARIS OBSERVATORY

Primarily these observations refer to the apparent movement of stars, independent of their actual motion. But it is obvious that the actual motion of the stars may complicate the backward drift, and that comparative data may enable the observer to separate one motion from the other. Then the spectroscopist steps in to test the line-of-sight motion of the star.

A combination of the two sets of observations reveals, finally, the actual movement of the star in three-dimensional space.

Collation of such records has revealed that, by and large, the stars are arranged in great groups or clusters, moving through space in various directions, like flocks of birds, or swarms of bees.

The great Dutch astronomer Kapteyn made laborious microscopic measurements of the location of about a quarter of a million stars on numberless photographic plates, and was thereby led to discover that two great star-streams, comprising not less than half a million members, including most of the brighter stars, have met and mingled like counter-currents in the region of space in which the solar system at present happens to be.

An Englishman, H. C. Plummer, made the same discovery through independent observation almost simultaneously.

These vast star-streams are moving in nearly opposite directions in the plane of the Milky Way. But they do not include the stars of the Milky Way itself. The myriad clusters that make up that galaxy lie far out beyond the star-streams. So distant are they that they show neither proper motion nor parallax nor actual motion. For the most part they are too faint to be tested accurately with the spectroscope.

The actual forms of the streams or clusters into which

they appear to be grouped are as yet only matters for conjecture. Their average distance is roughly computed at a neighborly three thousand light-years or so. Even at that, if they had been blotted out of existence in the days of the mightiest Pharaohs of Egypt, they would still shine for us just as they do.

If we view the galaxy of stars from yet another standpoint, asking what has been revealed as to the ultimate structure of the cosmic mechanism, we learn that a combination of methods, in the hands of many observers, has given some extraordinary glimpses into the arrangement of at least those portions of the universe that lie somewhat within our neighborhood.

Considering first our immediate environment in space, it appears that our sun, with its inconsequential planetary attendants, is one of a company of seventeen stars making up a rather compact cluster about ninety-five billion miles in diameter—roughly one million times the earth's distance from the sun. Seven of these stars are doubles. Five of them are brighter than the sun; yet all are comparatively dim, the brightest being only forty-eight times brighter than the sun; whereas there are more distant stars in the sky that are ten thousand times more brilliant.

Going out beyond the confines of our immediate star cluster, we find various interesting groups at what might be called—gaging our mind to stellar magnitudes—moderate distances.

There is, for example, a neighborly cluster of forty stars in the constellation Taurus, between the Pleiades and the bright yellow star Aldebaran, that Professor Lewis Boss, of Albany, watched with tireless assiduity for many years, using the proper motions alone, and not the spectrographic method. By laborious calcula-

tions he removed one source of error after another,
until finally he could assure us that the stars of the
Taurus cluster are moving through space together in
parallel lines at uniform speed, like a flock of birds.

They are 120 light-years (800 million million miles)
away; but they passed us at half that distance about
8,000 centuries ago — observed, perhaps, but not recorded by star-gazers of the Rough Stone Age.

Then there is a cluster of seventeen helium stars in
Perseus; and another cluster of thirteen stars in the
Great Bear, which seem to lie in about the same plane
—each cluster pursuing its own independent way, apparently quite unaffected by other stars that may chance
to have wandered into the same territory.

As to the Great Bear cluster, it is rather surprising
to learn that of the seven conspicuous stars forming the
"big dipper," five are moving uniformly in one direction and the other two with equal uniformity in quite
another direction.

The familiar figure of the "big dipper" is therefore
in part an optical illusion which will not maintain its
shape throughout future ages.

In due course the "pointers," for example, will cease
to point to the pole star. But the pole itself is shifting
as our little globe wabbles through space, so this does
not greatly matter. Some 12,000 years from now Vega
will be the pole star, and no pointers will be needed to
indicate that brilliant object. .

At far greater distances in space there are groups of
stars of the Orion or helium type, which have a charac-
teristic spectrum suggestive of a recent origin. These
are sometimes grouped into luminous clouds like the
Pleiades and the diffused nebulosity in Orion.

Some of these stars have enormous absolute brilliancy.

TWO VIEWS OF SATURN

Rigel in Orion, for example, shines at first magnitude. Were it no brighter than our sun it would appear only as a telescopic star of tenth magnitude.

We have just spoken of the dazzling brightness of some stars in comparison with our own particular star.

It must be explained, however, that brightness is not to be confused with actual mass. There is a rather definite, and for the astronomer highly useful, relation between volume and brightness, but a star of enormous size may be so tenuous in structure that its actual mass is no greater than that of a star of only a fraction its diameter.

This is obvious enough, but few astronomers, perhaps, suspected how entirely fallacious the test of size is in estimating the mass of a star until Professor Eddington made a computation in which, for graphic effect, he postulated a series of gaseous spheres, the first containing ten grams, the second one hundred grams, the third one thousand grams, and so on.

Number 1 weighs as much as a letter, number 5 as much as a man, number 10 as much as an ocean liner.

Nothing startling so far. But now, going up the scale, to reach numbers 30 and beyond, comes the surprise. For it appears that all the stars whose masses are known lie between numbers 33 and 35 of the scale. And nearly all lie between numbers 33 and 34.

Eddington's calculations show that, until we come to sphere 33, light-pressure is nearly negligible compared to gas expansion; and after we reach sphere 35, gas expansion is nearly negligible compared to light-pressure.

At this point, then, in Eddington's picturesque phrase, we should expect "something to happen." And "what happens is the stars."

Masses smaller than number 33 do not grow hot enough to shine. Masses larger than number 35 are too unstable because radiation pressure bursts them asunder.

Sphere 33 is of half the mass of the sun, and sphere 35 has fifty times the sun's mass.

In general terms, then, it may be said that a star whose mass is one-tenth that of the sun would never become a self-luminous body, tho it might exist as a dark star, while a mass one hundred times that of the sun either could not form at all, or would be broken up because the disruptive forces due to the high temperatures developed would exceed its gravitational force.

The astonishing tentative conclusion is, then, that luminous stars are limited in mass to a range of from about one-tenth the mass of our sun to one hundred times that mass.

It is pointed out that this theoretical calculation is sustained by the observation that the star of least mass known (at the moment) is, according to Aitken, of a mass one-fifth that of the sun, while the star of greatest mass is a double, with components approximately 86 and 72 times the sun's mass.

The smallest star in question is the companion of Krueger 60.

The heaviest star is known as B. D. plus 6° 1309. It may be more popularly described as Plaskett's star, having been discovered in 1922 by Professor J. S. Plaskett, of the Dominion Observatory.

Mr. Otto Struve's particular star, discovered in 1927, appears to be a quadruplet, with aggregate mass calculated as 950 times that of the sun. If confirmed, the mass of this star contradicts the Eddington calculation —or represents an exceptional departure from precedent.

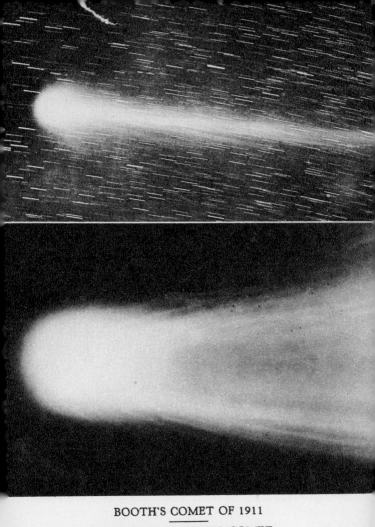

BOOTH'S COMET OF 1911

———

HEAD OF HALLEY'S COMET

Even so it appears that the words "giant" and "dwarf" apply to stars only in a relative sense. There is no such discrepancy in actual size of stars as there is in apparent size.

Of normal stars as of normal human beings, it might be said that all are of an "average" size.

Moreover, the greatest discrepancy between the smallest and largest stars (as hitherto computed) is no more than that between human beings at different stages of their career. There is this difference, however, that baby stars bulk large, while old stars are small. Giant stars are young and dwarfs are old. The giants make a brilliant appearance, but they are really great clouds of gas.

Now we begin to understand how it is that the brilliant Sirius gives 10,000 times more light than its dwarf companion, and yet is really only three times as heavy as the dwarf.

We have an inkling as to why stars of the same type —that is to say, the same age—tend to be grouped in the sky in great scattered clusters.

We can picture a time when each such cluster was a vast cloud of primordial gas, its portions being first drawn together by gravitation, and then, heated by this process, scattered by radiation into more or less isolated clouds, each of which ultimately underwent condensation to produce an individual star, or smaller group of stars.

We even have an inkling as to why, on the average, young stars are drifting through the universe at relatively slow speed, as compared with old stars—why, in a word, star speeds are progressively more rapid in the successive classes from O and B through the descending scale A, F, G, K, to M.

Campbell and Moore, for example, found the average

radial velocity of the B (young, hot) stars they examined to be 8.7 kilometers per second, while the M stars moved almost twice as fast—16.1 kilometers per second.

Correspondingly Boss, by observation of proper motions, found Class B stars moving 2.8 seconds of arc per century while M stars move 5.0 seconds per century.

Fath summarizes these facts with the statement that: The more massive stars have smaller velocities than the less massive. He adds, with true scientific caution, that we need additional facts before we shall have an adequate explanation.

Abandoning caution, one might suggest that the big young stars are nearer the stage when their substance was part of a vast cosmic cloud in which gravitation tending to pull the substance together and radiation tending to separate it oscillated and, as it were, fought for mastery. The old stars evidence that the battle was finally won by gravitation, which subsequently was to drive the stars, age after age, faster and faster in their fall toward some gravitational center of the universe, or in a comet-like circuit about such a hypothetical center. But this, of course, is purely conjectural.

Explanations aside, however, the facts of star-movement and star-clustering, accumulated through the joint endeavors of scores of modern observers, enable the more imaginative astronomers of our day to conceive at least in vague outline the scheme of the galactic system and of what they believe to be outlying portions of the universe.

The schemes of no two theorists precisely agree, yet there is basic uniformity in the conception of the watch-shaped galactic system, with the great body of the stars circling about its circumference.

Strömberg emphasizes the existence of a "preferential way" (somewhat along the plane of this system) through which great flocks of stars tend to migrate.

Easton sees in the galactic system a giant spiral nebula, with the center of the spiral somewhere in the direction of the constellation Cygnus.

In this view, our galaxy is one of the system of spiral nebulæ, rivaled in size perhaps only (in Shapley's view) by the companion "super-galaxy" Coma-Virgo—the other spirals being, to these, as islands to continents.

The "other spirals" in question are distributed (as we have seen) to the number of 100,000 or ten times that, about the poles of our galactic system. That is to say, they occupy the relatively starless spaces at right angles to the plane of the Milky Way.

Dr. H. D. Curtis, as cited by Dr. Abbot in his book *The Earth and the Stars,* presents an attractive diagram (here reproduced) of this scheme of the great spiral of the Milky Way, which we call the stellar universe, and these telescopic spirals which have come to be spoken of as "island universes."

The same conception is represented in pictorial diagram by a lens-shaped group of stars long familiar.

In November, 1929, Professor Harlow Shapley presented before the American Academy of Science an outline of perhaps the most comprehensive interpretation of the cosmic scheme hitherto attempted.

Professor Shapley estimates the diameter of our watch-shaped galaxy at about 300,000 light-years; with thickness at about 10,000 light-years.

He brings the objects of the entire universe into a serial scale, ranging from the world of the almost infinitely little to the world of the almost infinitely great.

THE FACTOR OF SPACE DISTRIBUTION
100,000 ± Spiral Nebulæ
Distance unknown

.
.
.
.
.
.
.
.
.

The Milky Way and stellar universe
is believed to be roughly lens-shaped and
about 3,000 by 30,000 or more light-years in
extent. In this space occur nearly all the stars, nearly all
the diffuse nebulosities, nearly all the planetary
nebulæ, nearly all new stars, nearly all clusters, nearly all the variable stars, etc., but
NO SPIRAL NEBULÆ

.
.
.
.
.
.
.

100,000 ± Spiral Nebulæ
Distance unknown

This graphic presentation of the universe-plan is credited to
Dr. H. D. Curtis by Dr. C. G. Abbot, from whose book *The
Earth and the Stars* it is here transcribed. A footnote states
that "Hubble has since proved that several spirals are about a
million light-years away." The word "proved" is perhaps in-
cautious.

At zero, as a starting point in either direction, he places the satellite system, of which our own earth-moon system is a type.

Grading downward, he ranges from meteoritic associations (comets, meteor streams, diffused nebulæ) through microscopic molecular aggregates to atoms and corpuscles.

Ranging upward successively are planetary structures (stars to ringed nebulæ), double and multiple stars, galactic clusters, globular clusters, star clouds, galaxies, super-galaxies (here our home galaxy), groups of super-galaxies, the "cosmoplasma" (cosmic meteors, diffused nebulosity, radiation), and the universe (the "space-time complex") as a whole.

That no one may suppose he thinks discovery at an end, Professor Shapley leaves a numbered blank space at each end of the series, to be filled in by investigators of the future.

Professor Shapley of course illustrates his system with a wealth of documentation.

Here it suffices to give the outline, and to note that a place is provided for every type of sidereal structure hitherto observed. A particularity of the scheme is the introduction of super-galaxies, of which the home galaxy is one; and of "groups of super-galaxies," which include double groups and complex assemblages.

Here, then, we have what might be called a documented and scientific elaboration of a scheme of minor and major systems of star groupings of which the genius of Johann Lambert had premonitory vision at the middle of the eighteenth century.

The system of the Milky Way, a flattened cylinder or spheroid; systems of higher order (our earth belonging "by a chain of gradations, to several systems, and at last to the system of the universe"); the Milky Way, comprehending several systems of fixed stars, each system with its own center; the "assemblages"—all these are adumbrated in the cosmologic dream of the contemporary of Wright and Kant, each of whom (it may be added) entertained not dissimilar dreams.

The difference is that the older cosmologists were groping in the dark, jumping to conclusions, drawing inferences from casual inspection of the stellar picture that could rank only as dreams —however close to inspiration.

But the modern cosmologist, elaborating these dreams of his forebears of the elder day, documents them, fortifies the speculations by an almost bewildering array of evidence garnered by new instrumental means—so that what was aforetime almost fantastic speculation becomes in our day secure (tho of course still provisional) scientific hypothesis.

In a word, the old cosmology was a vague fantasy, the new cosmology is a structure clearly depicted as to its major outlines.

But the new cosmology has nothing convincing to say about the ultimate plan of the structure whose details of movement are revealed on so large a scale.

Whether, as Lambert conceived, there is a common center about which all the bodies of the universe revolve—or, better said, all the universes—remains for the cosmologist of the future to determine.

AURORA BOREALIS

A HUGE METEORITE

VIII
THE ORIGIN OF THE WORLD

CENTURY marks are of course only arbitrary divisions of time. But they enter so constantly into human calculations that it is difficult not to regard them as actual milestones of progress. So it seems altogether fitting that a brand-new explanation of the origin of the solar system should have been one of the earliest contributions to theory and knowledge at the beginning of the twentieth century.

It is a doubly auspicious augury that the idea should have come out of America—as the first great contribution to the theory of world-making that has originated in the western hemisphere.

The new theory found its origin, or at least its chief tangible support, in the observations of a famous American astronomer, Professor Keeler, then director of the Lick Observatory. This keen-eyed observer devoted the last two years of his life (1898-1900) to the special investigation of that curious member of the celestial family, the nebula. Working with the famous three-foot telescope known as the Crossley reflector, Keeler found that the universe is thickly tenanted with nebulæ. He estimated that at least 120,000 of these bodies lay within the range of his vision as aided by the three-foot mirror. Several times that number are probably visible in the five-foot reflector since then installed at the Mt. Wilson Observatory.

Of course nebulæ were no new discovery. A certain

number of them had been observed ever since telescopes were invented. One or two are even faintly visible like misty stars, to the naked eye. But the importance of Professor Keeler's observations consisted (1) in showing the vast abundance of these curious structures, and (2) in revealing the very striking fact that a large preponderance of the nebulæ have a spiral structure. As the photographic film was made to supplement direct vision, revealing tenuosities of nebular structure that the eye cannot detect, it became increasingly evident that the spiral is, so to say, the typical form of nebulæ as a class. And this suggested some highly interesting questions as to method of world-building, as will appear in a moment.

Quite aside from their relation to world-making, however, these spiral nebulæ are telescopic objects of peculiar picturesqueness. They seem to be great luminous whirlpools of incandescent matter. Perhaps to the average eye they suggest more than anything else the popular and familiar type of firework called the pinwheel.

If you partially close your eyes and look at the photograph of a spiral nebula you can easily imagine that it represents a whirligig of fire, two revolving points making a pair of entwined incandescent spirals, and the sputtering flames sending out clouds of sparks and luminous smoke in an ever-widening circle.

Now, in point of fact, something very like this is the interpretation which the astronomer puts upon the spiral nebula. He believes that its central luminous nucleus is an incandescent gaseous body like our sun, and that the two spirals that lead out from it, with their irregularly scattered foci of light, and their filmy veils of luminous smoke, represent matter that has burst forth from the central body, and that is now revolving upon the central axis very much as the pin-wheel revolves about its central pin.

Only, of course, the axis in this case is an imaginary body, like the axis of our sun or the earth's pole, and the span of the entire nebula is to be measured in unthinkable millions of miles.

There is a nebula in the constellation of Andromeda that is estimated to be so wide that light requires about fifty thousand years to span it. (This new estimate supplants the older estimate of *eight* years—illustrating the expansion of ideas in the contemporary epoch.) It is faintly visible to the naked eye.

Regardless of size, however, what gives the spiral nebula interest from the present standpoint is the fact that nebulæ have long been regarded as the matrix out of which solar systems such as ours are developed.

For about a hundred years astronomers had held as stock doctrine the theory of Laplace, according to which our solar system originated from a superheated gaseous globe which contracted as it cooled, and from time to time threw off rings of its equatorial substance that became planets.

But Professor Keeler's nebulæ seemed to contradict this theory. The spiral nebula quite obviously is not a uniformly gaseous mass. There is filmy, tenuous matter permeating its structure, but its main substance seems to be composed of more or less discrete nodules or nuclei.

Professor Keeler himself noted this discrepancy, but it remained for Professor T. C. Chamberlin, of the University of Chicago, and his younger colleague, Professor T. R. Moulton, to take the matter up and develop a new theory of world-making—a theory based on ob-

ETNA IN ACTION

CRATERS AT ETNA AFTER ERUPTION

servation of the spiral nebula, but harmonized with all the new facts of astronomy and geology that had come to contradict the old hypothesis.

The new theory assumes that the typical spiral nebula, as revealed to us by the telescope, is in fact the parent structure of a solar system such as ours.

Stated otherwise, it assumes that our solar system was once a spiral nebula differing only in size from any one of the hundreds of thousands of such bodies that still tenant the universe. It further assumes that the clustered masses to be seen here and there along the arms of the spiral nebula (knots in the skein, Professor Chamberlin has suggestively called them) are nuclei out of which will ultimately develop a group of planets more or less similar to those that constitute the sun's family.

A spiral nebula then, in this view, is a system of worlds in the making.

The central nucleus is the future sun. Various of the spots that lie along the arms of the spiral are the nuclei of future planets. Professor Chamberlin calls nuclei of all sizes "planetesimals" because they are supposed to be revolving in independent orbits, like miniature planets. Hence the name "planetesimal theory."

It is obvious at a glance that the larger nuclei—bigger fragments of world stuff—make up the structure of the spiral arms. It is possible that matter is streaming along these arms as it appears to be. In any case, the entire structure is revolving as if it were a solid body. The larger nuclei, however, necessarily exert a gravitational influence over the smaller planetesimals in their neighborhood; hence an incessant shower of smaller particles will fall against each larger nucleus and this augments its size and its gravitational power.

As time goes on, each of these growing nuclei will

VESUVIUS IN ERUPTION

(through gravitation) suck in the matter from the space about it, as a vacuum cleaner sucks in dust, until ultimately each larger body will be revolving in a clear space.

Thus the myriads of planetesimals will have been aggregated into a small number of planets; and the spiral nebula will have been developed into a planetary system. The original central nucleus of the nebula, having drawn to itself the cloud of minor planetesimals in its neighborhood, becomes a detached central sun.

According to this theory, then, our earth, in common with its sister planets, was never a gaseous ring, nor yet a liquid globe; but was built up about a more or less solid nucleus by a perpetual meteoric bombardment.

Larger planets of our system may have gathered matter so rapidly, thanks to their greater gravitational power, as to super-heat their substance to the stage of liquidity or gaseousness.

Such according to some theorists is still the condition of Jupiter and Saturn and probably also of Uranus and Neptune. Unless, indeed, Jupiter is ice-cold, as some recent heat-tests appear to suggest—which would be quite accordant with the planetesimal theory.

In any event our earth and the other smaller planets were probably from the beginning solid in structure, tho doubtless developing a high interior temperature through impact and compression. Their growth would be decreasingly rapid as the outlying planetesimal matter within their sphere was more nearly exhausted. But their growth continues, in a minor degree, even now; for it is well known that the earth sweeps up something like a hundred million meteors each day—these meteors being, supposedly, belated fragments of the original spiral nebula.

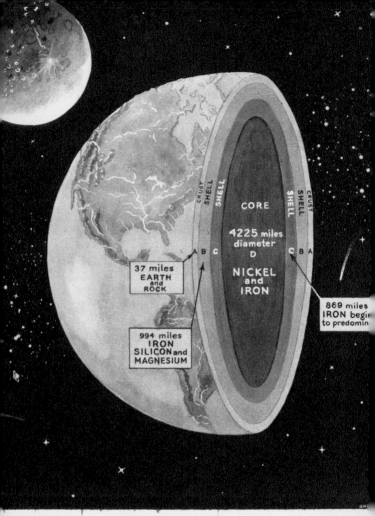

THE EARTH'S INTERIOR

IX

STRUCTURE OF THE EARTH

THE planetesimal theory finds support in the fact that the center of the earth is much heavier than the exterior. This was first demonstrated, as long ago as the year 1774, by an Astronomer Royal of England, Nevil Maskelyne. The demonstration was made by a curious experiment that has been spoken of as weighing a mountain. Incidentally, until this test was made, it had been commonly believed that the interior of the earth was composed of water.

What Maskelyne did, technically stated, was to test the gravitation-pull of a mountain against that of the globe. The effect, or the accomplished act, was the weighing of the earth.

The practical method employed was to test the deflection of a plumb-line on either side of an abruptly-rising "hog-back" mountain. A plumb-line is supposed to point directly toward the center of the earth. But in fact it was discovered that when the line is swung in the neighborhood of a mountain, the gravitation-pull of the mountain deflects the plumb-line, so that it does not actually point directly toward the center of the earth. But there is only one way in which this slight deflection can be detected, and that is by adjusting the line to a telescope and directing the telescope toward a fixed star.

The plumb-line determines the zenith, and the direction of the telescope determines the angle of distance of the star from the zenith.

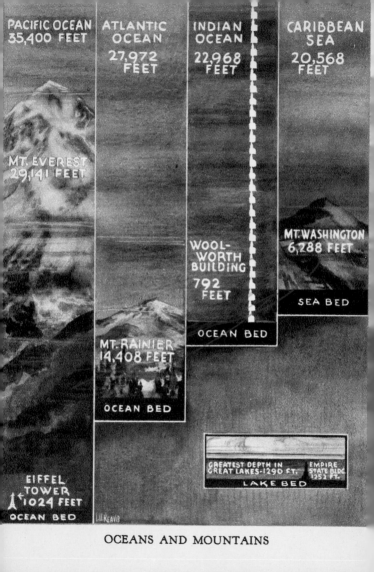

OCEANS AND MOUNTAINS

When Maskelyne set up his telescope first on one side and then on the other of a narrow "hog-back" mountain, he discovered that the zenith distance of the star was different, as observed from the two sides of the mountain. Since the star could not have shifted, it followed that the zenith, or apparent zenith, had shifted. And this is another way of saying that the plumb-line, which determines the zenith, had been deflected.

By making a computation of the size—that is to say, the bulk—of the mountain, and calculating its mass as compared with the mass of the earth, the problem of weighing the earth was solved. The principle involved is simply that of the so-called inverse squares, according to which all masses of matter attract each other in direct proportion to the mass and inversely as the square of the distance. This, of course, is the now familiar principle of gravitation.

The known factors in Maskelyne's experiment were the mass of the mountain and the size of the earth. The mass of the mountain could be directly estimated. The mass of the earth was the unknown factor which was determined by the experiment. The solution showed that the earth, as a whole, has a mass about twice what it would have if its entire structure were no heavier than the rocky structure of a mountain.

Not very long after Maskelyne's test was made, another Englishman, Thomas Cavendish, devised a different method of weighing the world, based, however, on the same principle. He suspended a very small ball near a large one, and noted the deflection caused by the attraction between the two bodies. This experiment, elaborated, is the one still employed in the modern physical laboratory in "weighing the world."

The newer tests are in agreement with the original

one of Maskelyne, leaving no doubt that the center of the earth is a very heavy mass of matter. The explanation usually accepted is that the center of the earth is made up very largely of iron, or of iron mixed with nickel. This estimate is corroborated by numberless tests with the seismograph or earthquake detector. These observations show that the rate of transmission of vibrations through the center of the earth is different from the transmission of the same vibrations along the surface of the earth.

The planetesimal theory of the origin of the world is in harmony with this conception of the heavy pull of our planet. It also gains support from the fact that meteorites falling to the earth are found to be composed largely of iron and nickel. There is another type of meteorite composed largely of rocky matter, but those of the more usual type, and particularly the very large meteorites, are of a metallic structure closely similar to what is believed to be the structure of the central core of the earth.

On the new theory, it is improbable that the earth was ever a liquid body. It was, however, a very hot body, and it is more than probable that the exterior was heated to the point of liquidity and so continued until a relatively recent geological period. The phrase "relatively recent" demands immediate explanation, however, for, according to the current estimates of the age of the earth, the time when the outer mass cooled sufficiently to become solid must be estimated at something like three billion years ago. This estimate is based on an analysis of the deposits of radioactive matter found here and there in the earth's strata. The heaviest of known elements, uranium, degenerates through a series of materials, of which radium is one, ultimately reaching an end product that is a type of lead. Physicists have computed the rate of breaking up of the uranium atom, and it is possible to make a computation as to the minimum age of any rocky substance in which such a deposit of uranium and lead is found. Such an analysis, applied to many different types of rock, has demonstrated that the age of geological strata is vastly in excess of what the early geologists supposed. According to the estimates of Lord Kelvin, made about half a century ago, the earth's crust was supposed to be only from sixty to one hundred million years old. The newer estimates, as suggested, extend the period to upward of three billion years.

It is believed that the solid crust of the earth at present extends only to the depth of forty or fifty miles. At this depth and below it for some hundreds of miles, the substance of the earth is believed to be in effect liquid, like molten glass—altho under such high pressure as to assume a different character from what we commonly think of as the liquid state. In this view, the continents are like islands, or, better stated, like rafts, floating in a heavier liquid.

The substance of which the continents are made has been called *sial,* and the liquid magma in which they float is named *sima.* The first word is an abbreviation of silicon-aluminum, and the second an abbreviation of silicon-magnesium. These words were introduced a good many years ago, but have not yet gained popularity.

The idea that the continents change their positions was put forward by a German, Alfred Wegener, about the year 1910. The present writer, in a book called *The Biography of Mother Earth,* attempted to explain how and why the whirling motion of the earth results in the movement of the continental masses in one direction or another, to establish equilibrium of the earth's mass as a whole. According to the theory put forward in this

EROSION BY WAVES OF THE SEA

book, the original continental mass was in the southern hemisphere, whence the continents have drifted northward to their present position.

Regardless of the theories as to the origin of the continents, however, there is an enormous series of facts as to the changes that have taken place in the structure of the continents themselves during the geological ages. The forces that have operated in the past to modify the continental surfaces, are those that are still operating today —wind, water, and chemical activity. The rocky structures that we see now elevated into mountains and plateaus are made up of strata that were originally deposited beneath water. This implies that the continental masses have risen and sunk from time to time. As to that, there is no difference of opinion among geologists.

The building up of new material in the ocean depths is largely the work of living organisms, often microscopic in size; these deposit their shells to form an ooze in the ocean depths which ultimately becomes hardened into stone. Mingled with this is the detritus of matter brought down in the rivers, which wash away rock and soil and gradually wear down even the highest mountains.

According to the theory of isostacy, first put forward by Clarence Dutton, it is the accumulated waste of such detritus at the borders of the continents that ultimately causes the up-bulging of the central continental masses. The forming of mountains is believed to be due, not to the shrinking of the earth's crust, as formerly supposed, but either to this pressure on the borders of the continents or, according to the Wegenerian hypothesis of the displacement of continents, in response to the resistance that the continental mass encounters in moving through the heavier magma in which it floats.

Mountains as we see them today are of two types. The

more familiar type, as represented by the Appalachians in eastern North America and the Rockies and Sierra Nevadas at the west, represent actual folding of strata— wrinklings of the earth's crust. A less familiar type of mountain may be seen in the western regions, notably in Arizona and New Mexico, where the strata of the earth have been elevated far above the water level without being folded. The action of the water has washed away a great part of the strata, leaving here and there flat-topped pyramidal mountains that are known as mesas. The explanation is that the top of such a mountain consists of a harder stratum of rock, which has resisted the action of the elements.

The action of water in eroding is illustrated on a magnificent scale in the Grand Canyon of the Colorado, and on a less spectacular scale in multitudes of canyons of lesser magnitude. In effect, the entire surface of the earth is a panorama which shows the action of the elements.

According to the new theory of continental displacement, the continental masses now in the northern hemisphere were floating northward across the equatorial regions in that early geological day when the coal beds were forming—through deposit of decaying vegetation— vast lagoons. The presence of coal beds in far northern regions, including Alaska and Greenland, is thus explained. The finding of coal deposits in the Antarctic Continent, verified by Admiral Byrd, confirms the belief that regions now near the pole were formerly located in subtropical or tropical regions. The continental mass has migrated to its present position, probably, in relatively recent times, geologically speaking, perhaps to balance the ice-cap that formed in the polar region during the most recent of the great glacial epochs.

X

EARLIER STUDIES OF THE EARTH'S CRUST

A CLEAR comprehension of the meaning and interpretation of the observed phenomena of the earth's crust was first gained, toward the close of the eighteenth century, by Dr. James Hutton, of Edinburgh, physician, farmer, and manufacturing chemist; patient, enthusiastic, level-headed devotee of science.

Inspired by his love of chemistry to study the character of rocks and soils, Hutton had not gone far before the earth stood revealed to him in a new light. He saw, what generations of predecessors had blindly refused to see, that the fact of nature everywhere, instead of being rigid and immutable, is perennially plastic, and year by year is undergoing metamorphic changes. The solidest rocks are day by day disintegrated, slowly, but none the less surely, by wind and rain and frost, by mechanical attrition and chemical decomposition, to form the pulverized earth and clay. This soil is being swept away by perennial showers, and carried off to the oceans. The oceans themselves beat on their shores, and eat insidiously into the structure of sands and rocks. Everywhere, slowly but surely, the surface of the land is being worn away; its substance being carried to burial in the seas.

Should this denudation continue long enough, thinks Hutton, the entire surface of the continents must be worn away. Should it be continued *long enough!* And with that thought there flashes on his mind an inspiring conception—the idea that solar time is long, indefinitely

EROSION BY WATER, WIND, AND
CHEMICAL ACTION

long. That seems a simple enough thought—almost a truism—to the twentieth-century mind, but it required genius to conceive it in the eighteenth. Hutton pondered it, grasped its full import, and made it the basis of his hypothesis, his "theory of the earth."

The hypothesis is this—that the observed changes of the surface of the earth, continued through indefinite lapses of time, must result in conveying all the land at last to the sea; in wearing continents away till the oceans overflow them. What then? Why, as the continents wear down, the oceans are filling up. Along their bottoms the detritus of wasted continents is deposited in strata, together with the bodies of marine animals and vegetables. Why might not this débris solidify to form layers of rocks—the basis of new continents? Why not, indeed?

But have we any proof that such formation of rocks in an ocean-bed has, in fact, occurred? To be sure, we have. It is furnished by every bed of limestone, every outcropping fragment of fossil-bearing rock, every stratified cliff. How else than through such formation in an ocean-bed came these rocks to be stratified? How else came they to contain the shells of once living organisms embedded in their depths? The ancients, finding fossil shells embedded in the rocks, explained them as mere freaks of "nature and the stars." Less superstitious generations had repudiated this explanation, but had failed to give a tenable solution of the mystery. To Hutton it is a mystery no longer. To him it seems clear that the basis of the present continents was laid in ancient sea-beds, formed of the detritus of continents yet more ancient.

But two links are still wanting to complete the chain of Hutton's hypothesis. Through what agency has the ooze of the ocean-bed been transformed into solid rock? And through what agency has this rock been lifted above

A TYPICAL "TWISTER" TORNADO

the surface of the water, to form new continents? Hutton looks about him for a clue, and soon he finds it. Everywhere about us there are outcropping rocks that are not stratified, but which give evidence to the observant eye of having once been in a molten state. Different minerals are mixed together; pebbles are scattered through masses of rock like plums in a pudding; irregular crevices in otherwise solid masses of rock—so-called veinings—are seen to be filled with equally solid granite of a different variety, which can have gotten there in no conceivable way, so Hutton thinks, but by running in while molten, as liquid metal is run into the moulds of the founder. Even the stratified rocks, tho they seemingly have not been melted, give evidence in some instances of having been subjected to the action of heat. Marble, for example, is clearly nothing but calcined limestone.

With such evidence before him, Hutton is at no loss to complete his hypothesis. The agency which has solidified the ocean-beds, he says, is subterranean heat. The same agency, acting excessively, has produced volcanic cataclysms, upheaving ocean-beds to form continents. The rugged and uneven surfaces of mountains, the tilted and broken character of stratified rocks everywhere, are the standing witnesses of these gigantic upheavals.

And with this the imagined cycle is complete. The continents, worn away and carried to the sea by the action of the elements, have been made over into rocks again in the ocean-beds, and then raised once more into continents. And this massive cycle, in Hutton's scheme, is supposed to have occurred not once only, but over and over again, times without number. In this unique view ours is indeed a world without beginning and without end; its continents have been making and unmaking in endless series since time began.

ANOTHER TORNADO

Hutton formulated his hypothesis while yet a young man, not long after the middle of the century. He first gave it publicity in 1781, in a paper before the Royal Society of Edinburgh, a paper which at the moment neither friend nor foe deigned to notice. It was not published in book form till the last decade of the century, when Hutton had lived with and worked over his theory for almost fifty years. Then it caught the eye of the world. A school of followers expounded the Huttonian doctrines; a rival school, under Werner, in Germany, opposed some details of the hypothesis; and the educated world as a whole viewed disputants askance. The very novelty of the new views forbade their immediate acceptance. Bitter attacks were made upon the "heresies," and that was meant to be a soberly tempered judgment which in 1800 pronounced Hutton's theories "not only hostile to sacred history, but equally hostile to the principles of probability, to the results of the ablest observations on the mineral kingdom, and to the dictates of rational philosophy." And all this because Hutton's theory presupposed the earth to have been in existence more than six thousand years.

Thus it appears that tho the thoughts of men had widened, in these closing days of the eighteenth century, to include the stars, they had not as yet expanded to receive the most patent records that are written everywhere on the surface of the earth. Before Hutton's views could be accepted, his pivotal conception that time is long must be established by convincing proofs. The evidence was being gathered by William Smith, Cuvier, and other devotees of the budding science of paleontology in the last days of the century, but the record of their completed labors belongs to another epoch.

Even the lucid *Illustrations of the Huttonian Theory,*

WATER EROSION IN PLATTE CANYON, COLORADO

which Playfair, the pupil and friend of the great Scotsman, published in 1802, did not at once prove convincing. The world had become enamored of the rival theory of Hutton's famous contemporary, Werner of Saxony —the theory which taught that "in the beginning" all the solids of the earth's present crust were dissolved in the heated waters of a universal sea. Werner affirmed that all rocks, of whatever character, had been formed by precipitation from this sea, as the waters cooled; that even veins have originated in this way; and that mountains are gigantic crystals, not upheaved masses. In a word, he practically ignored volcanic action, and denied in toto the theory of metamorphosis of rocks through the agency of heat.

The followers of Werner came to be known as Neptunists; the Huttonians as Plutonists. The history of geology during the first quarter of the nineteenth century is mainly a recital of the intemperate controversy between these opposing schools; tho it should not be forgotten that, meantime, the members of the Geological Society of London were making an effort to hunt for facts and avoid compromising theories. Fact and theory, however, were too closely linked to be thus divorced.

The brunt of the controversy settled about the unstratified rocks—granites and their allies—which the Plutonists claimed as of igneous origin. This contention had the theoretical support of the nebular hypothesis, then gaining ground, which supposed the earth to be a cooling globe. The Plutonists laid great stress, too, on the observed fact that the temperature of the earth increases at a pretty constant ratio as descent toward its center is made in mines. But in particular they appealed to the phenomena of volcanoes.

The evidence from this source was gathered and elab-

EROSION ON A TITANIC SCALE. NIAGARA FALLS

orated by G. Poulett Scrope, secretary of the Geological Society of England, who, in 1823, published a classical work on volcanoes, in which he claimed that volcanic mountains, including some of the highest known peaks, are merely accumulated masses of lava belched forth from a crevice in the earth's crust. The Neptunists stoutly contended for the aqueous origin of volcanic as of other mountains.

But the facts were with Scrope, and as time went on it came to be admitted that not merely volcanoes, but many "trap" formations not taking the form of craters had been made by the obtrusion of molten rock through fissures in overlying strata. Such, for example, to cite familiar illustrations, are Mount Holyoke, in Massachusetts, and the well-known formation of the Palisades along the Hudson.

But to admit the "Plutonic" origin of such widespread formations was practically to abandon the Neptunian hypothesis. So gradually the Huttonian explanation of the origin of granites and other "igneous" rocks, whether massed or in veins, came to be accepted. Most geologists then came to think of the earth as a molten mass, on which the crust rests as a mere film. Some, indeed, with Lyell, prefer to believe that the molten areas exist only as lakes in a solid crust, heated to melting perhaps, by electrical or chemical action, as Davy suggested. More recently a popular theory attempts to reconcile geological facts with the claim of the physicists, that the earth's entire mass is at least as rigid as steel, by supposing that a molten film rests between the observed solid crust and the alleged solid nucleus. But be that as it may, the theory that subterranean heat has been instrumental in determining the condition of "primary" rocks, and in producing many other phenomena of the earth's

crust, has never been in dispute since the long controversy between the Neptunists and the Plutonists led to
its establishment.

If molten matter exists beneath the crust of the earth,
it must contract in cooling, and in so doing it must dis-
turb the level of the portion of the crust already solidified. So a plausible explanation of the upheaval of continents and mountains was supplied by the Plutonian
theory, as Hutton had from the first alleged. But now an
important difference of opinion arose as to the exact
rationale of such upheavals. Hutton himself, and practically every one else who accepted his theory, had supposed that there are long periods of relative repose, during which the level of the crust is undisturbed, followed
by short periods of active stress, when continents are
thrown up with volcanic suddenness, as by the throes of
a gigantic earthquake. But now came Charles Lyell with
his famous extension of the "uniformitarian" doctrine,
claiming that past changes of the earth's surface have
been like present changes in degree as well as in kind.
The making of continents and mountains, he said, is
going on as rapidly today as at any time in the past.
There have been no gigantic cataclysmic upheavals at
any time, but all changes in level of the strata as a
whole have been gradual, by slow oscillation, or at most
by repeated earthquake shocks such as are still often
experienced.

In support of this very startling contention Lyell
gathered a mass of evidence of the recent changes in
level of continental areas. He corroborated by personal
inspection the claim which had been made by Playfair
in 1802, and by von Buch in 1807, that the coast-line
of Sweden is rising at the rate of from a few inches to
several feet in a century. He cited Darwin's observations

going to prove that Patagonia is similarly rising, and
Pingel's claim that Greenland is slowly sinking. Proof
as to sudden changes of level of several feet, over large
areas, due to earthquakes, was brought forward in
abundance. Cumulative evidence left it no longer open
to question that such oscillatory changes of level, either
upward or downward, are quite the rule, and it could
not be denied that these observed changes, if continued
long enough in one direction, would produce the highest
elevations. The possibility that the making of even the
highest ranges of mountains had been accomplished without exaggerated catastrophic action came to be freely
admitted.

It became clear that the supposedly stable land surfaces are in reality much more variable than the surface
of the "shifting sea"; that continental masses, seemingly
so fixed, are really rising and falling in billows thousands
of feet in height, ages instead of moments being consumed in the sweep between crest and hollow.

These slow oscillations of land surfaces being understood, many geological enigmas were made clear—such
as the alternation of marine and fresh-water formations
in a vertical series, which Cuvier and Brongniart had
observed near Paris; or the sandwiching of layers of
coal, of subaerial formation, between layers of subaqueous
clay or sandstone, which may be observed everywhere
in the coal measures. In particular, the extreme thickness
of the sedimentary strata as a whole, many times exceeding the depth of the deepest known sea, was for the
first time explicable when it was understood that such
strata had formed in slowly sinking ocean-beds.

All doubt as to the mode of origin of stratified rocks being thus removed, the way was opened for a more favor-
able consideration of that other Huttonian doctrine of

SAND DUNES IN ALGERIA. ACTION OF THE WIND

EROSION IN THE ARIZONA DESERT, EXPOSING
PETRIFIED TREE-TRUNKS

the extremely slow denudation of land surfaces. The enormous amount of land erosion will be patent to any one who uses his eyes intelligently in a mountain district. It will be evident in any region where the strata are tilted—as, for example, the Alleghanies—that great folds of strata which must once have risen miles in height have in many cases been worn entirely away, so that now a valley marks the location of the former eminence. Where the strata are level, as in the case of the mountains of Sicily, the Scotch Highlands, and the familiar Catskills, the evidence of denudation is, if possible, even more marked; for here it is clear that elevation and valley have been carved by the elements out of land that rose from the sea as level plateaus.

But that this herculean labor of land-sculpturing could have been accomplished by the slow action of wind and frost and shower was an idea few men could grasp within the first half-century after Hutton propounded it; nor did it begin to gain general currency until Lyell's crusade against catastrophism, begun about 1830, had for a quarter of a century accustomed geologists to the thought of slow continuous changes producing final results of colossal proportions. And even long after that, it was combated by such men as Murchison, Director-General of the Geological Survey of Great Britain, then accounted the foremost field-geologist of his time, who continued to believe that the existing valleys owe their main features to subterranean forces of upheaval. Even Murchison, however, made some recession from the belief of the Continental authorities, Elie de Beaumont and Leopold von Buch, who contended that the mountains had sprung up like veritable jacks-in-the box. Von Buch, whom his friend and fellow-pupil von Humboldt considered the foremost geologist of the time, died in 1853,

OLD FAITHFUL GEYSER, YELLOWSTONE
NATIONAL PARK

still firm in his early faith that the erratic boulders found high on the Jura had been hurled there, like cannon-balls, across the valley of Geneva by the sudden up-heaval of a neighboring mountain range.

The boulders whose presence on the crags of the Jura the old German accounted for in a manner so theatrical had long been a source of contention among geologists. They are found not merely on the Jura, but on number-less other mountains in all north-temperate latitudes, and often far out in the open country, as many a farmer who has broken his plow against them might testify. The early geologists accounted for them, as for nearly everything else, with their supposititious Deluge. Brong-niart and Cuvier and Buckland and their contempora-ries appeared to have no difficulty in conceiving that masses of granite weighing hundreds of tons had been swept by this current scores or hundreds of miles from their source. But of course the uniformitarian faith permitted no such explanation, nor could it countenance the projection idea; so Lyell was bound to find some other means of transportation for the puzzling erratics.

The only available medium was ice, but fortunately this one seemed quite sufficient. Icebergs, said Lyell, are observed to carry all manner of débris, and deposit it in the sea-bottoms. Present land surfaces have often been submerged beneath the sea. During the latest of these submergences icebergs deposited the boulders now scat-tered here and there over the land. Nothing could be simpler or more clearly uniformitarian. And even the catastrophists, tho they met Lyell amicably on almost no other theoretical ground, were inclined to admit the plausibility of his theory of erratics. Indeed, of all Lyell's non-conformist doctrines, this seemed the one most likely to meet with general acceptance.

EROSION BY RAIN AND WIND. PEAKS OF
THE SIERRAS

THE CANADIAN ROCKIES

Yet, even as this iceberg theory loomed large and larger before the geological world, observations were making in a different field that were destined to show its fallacy. As early as 1815 a sharp-eyed chamois-hunter of the Alps, Perraudin by name, had noted the existence of the erratics, and, unlike most of his companion hunters, had puzzled his head as to how the boulders got where he saw them. He knew nothing of submerged continents or of icebergs, still less of upheaving mountains; and tho he doubtless had heard of the Flood, he had no experience of heavy rocks floating like corks in water. Moreover, he had never observed stones rolling up hill and perching themselves on mountain-tops, and he was a good enough uniformitarian (tho he would have been puzzled indeed had any one told him so) to disbelieve that stones in past times had disported themselves differently in this regard from stones of the present. Yet there the stones are. How did they get there?

The mountaineer thought that he could answer that question. He saw about him those gigantic serpent-like streams of ice called glaciers, "from their far fountains slow rolling on," carrying with them blocks of granite and other débris to form moraine deposits. If these glaciers had once been much more extensive than they now are, they might have carried the boulders and left them where we find them. On the other hand, no other natural agency within the sphere of the chamois-hunter's knowledge could have accomplished this, ergo the glaciers must once have been more extensive. Perraudin would probably have said that common-sense drove him to this conclusion; but be that as it may, he had conceived one of the few truly original and novel ideas of which the nineteenth century can boast.

MUIR GLACIER, ALASKA

MOUNT RAINIER, "GIBRALTAR ROCK"

Perraudin announced his idea to the greatest scientist in his little world—Jean de Charpentier, director of the mines at Bex, a skilled geologist who had been a fellow-pupil of von Buch and von Humboldt under Werner at the Freiberg School of Mines. Charpentier laughed at the mountaineer's grotesque idea, and thought no more about it. And ten years elapsed before Perraudin could find any one who treated his notion with greater respect. Then he found a listener in M. Venetz, a civil engineer, who read a paper on the novel glacial theory before a local society in 1823. This brought the matter once more to the attention of Charpentier, who now felt that there might be something in it worth investigation.

A survey of the field in the light of the new theory soon convinced Charpentier that the chamois-hunter had all along been right. He became an enthusiastic supporter of the idea that the Alps had once been embedded in a mass of ice, and in 1836 he brought the notion to the attention of Louis Agassiz, who was spending the summer in the Alps. Agassiz was skeptical at first, but soon became a convert. Then he saw that the implications of the theory extended far beyond the Alps. If the Alps had been covered with an ice sheet, so had many other regions of the northern hemisphere. Casting abroad for evidences of glacial action, Agassiz found them everywhere, in the form of transported erratics, scratched and polished outcropping rocks, and moraine-like deposits. Presently he became convinced that the ice sheet which covered the Alps had spread over the whole of the higher latitudes of the northern hemisphere, forming an ice cap over the globe. Thus the common-sense induction of the chamois-hunter blossomed in the mind of Agassiz into the conception of a universal Ice Age.

GLACIER FORMING FUTURE ICEBERGS

ICEBERG ADRIFT

In 1857 Agassiz introduced his theory to the world, in a paper read at Neuchâtel, and three years later he published his famous *Etudes sur les Glaciers*. Never did idea make a more profound disturbance in the scientific world. Von Buch treated it with alternate ridicule, contempt, and rage; Murchison opposed it with customary vigor; even Lyell, whose most remarkable mental endowment was an unfailing receptiveness to new truths, could not at once discard his iceberg theory in favor of the new claimant. Dr. Buckland, however, after Agassiz had shown him evidence of former glacial action in his own Scotland, became a convert—the more readily, perhaps, as it seemed to him to oppose the uniformitarian idea. Gradually others fell in line, and after the usual embittered controversy and the inevitable full generation of probation, the idea of an Ice Age took its place among the accepted tenets of geology. All manner of moot points still demanded attention—the cause of the Ice Age, the exact extent of the ice sheet, the precise manner in which it produced its effects, and the exact nature of these effects; and not all of these have even yet been determined. But, details aside, the Ice Age now has full recognition from geologists as an historical period. There may have been many Ice Ages, as Dr. Croll contends; there was surely one; and the conception of such a period is one of the very few ideas of our century that no previous century had even so much as faintly adumbrated.

At its climax the ice sheet extended southward to about the fortieth parallel, driving some animals before it, and destroying those that were unable to migrate. At its fulness, the great ice mass lay almost a mile in depth over New England, as attested by the scratched and polished rock surfaces and deposited erratics in the White

MORAINE ON EAST SIDE OF GLACIER BAY, ALASKA

ROBERTSON GLACIER, GREENLAND

Mountains. Such a mass presses down with a weight of about one hundred and twenty-five tons to the square foot, according to Dr. Croll's estimate. It crushed and ground everything beneath it more or less, and in some regions planed off hilly surfaces into prairies. Creeping slowly forward, it carried all manner of débris with it. When it melted away its terminal moraine built up the nucleus of the land masses now known as Long Island and Staten Island; other of its deposits formed the "drumlins" about Boston famous as Bunker and Breeds hills; and it left a long irregular line of ridges of "till" of boulder clay and scattered erratics clear across the country at about the latitude of New York City.

As the ice sheet slowly receded it left minor moraines all along its course. Sometimes its deposits dammed up river courses or inequalities in the surface, to form the lakes which everywhere abound over Northern territories. Some glacialists even hold the view first suggested by Ramsey, of the British Geological Survey, that the great glacial sheet scooped out the basins of many lakes, including the system that feeds the Saint Lawrence. At all events, it left traces of its presence all along the line of its retreat, and its remnants exist to this day as mountain glaciers and the polar ice cap. Indeed, we live on the border of the last glacial epoch, for with the closing of this period the long geologic past merges into the present.

And the present, no less than the past, is a time of change . That is the thought which James Hutton conceived more than a century ago, but which his contemporaries and successors were so very slow to appreciate. Now, however, it has become axiomatic — one can hardly realize that it was ever doubted. Every new scientific truth, says Agassiz, must pass through three

POLISHED BY THE ICE-SHEET

GROUND AND GOUGED BY ICE

stages—first, men say it is not true; then they declare
it hostile to religion; finally, they assert that every one
has known it always. Hutton's truth that natural law
is changeless and eternal has reached this final stage.
Nowhere now could you find a scientist who would dispute the truth of that text which Lyell, quoting from
Playfair's *Illustrations of the Huttonian Theory,* printed
on the title-page of his *Principles:* "Amid all the revolutions of the globe the economy of Nature has been uniform, and her laws are the only things that have resisted
the general movement. The rivers and the rocks, the
seas and the continents, have been changed in all their
parts; but the laws which direct those changes, and the
rules to which they are subject, have remained invari-
ably the same."

But, on the other hand, Hutton and Playfair, and in
particular Lyell, drew inferences from this principle
which the modern physicist can by no means admit. To
them it implied that the changes on the surface of the
earth have always been the same in degree as well as
in kind, and must so continue while present forces hold
their sway. In other words, they thought of the world
as a great perpetual-motion machine. But the modern
physicist, given truer mechanical insight by the doctrines of the conservation and the dissipation of energy,
will have none of that. Lord Kelvin, in particular, has
urged that in the periods of our earth's infancy and
adolescence its developmental changes must have been,
like those of any other infant organism, vastly more
rapid and pronounced than those of a later day; and to
every clear thinker this truth also must now seem axiomatic.

Whoever thinks of the earth as a cooling (even if
never liquid) globe can hardly doubt that its crust, when

TRANSPORTED BY THE ICE-SHEET.
GRANITE BOULDERS

thinner, may have heaved under strain of the moon's tidal pull—whether or not that body was nearer—into great billows, daily rising and falling, like waves of the present seas vastly magnified.

Under stress of that same lateral pressure which now produces the slow depression of the Jersey coast, the slow rise of Sweden, the occasional belching of an insignificant volcano, the jetting of a geyser, or the trembling of an earthquake, once large areas were rent in twain, and vast floods of lava flowed over thousands of square miles of the earth's surface perhaps at a single jet; and, for aught we know to the contrary, gigantic mountains may have heaped up their contorted heads in cataclysms as spasmodic as even the most ardent catastrophist of the elder day of geology could have imagined.

The atmosphere of that early day, filled with vast volumes of carbon, oxygen, and other chemicals that have since been stored in beds of coal, limestone and granites, may have worn down the rocks, on the one hand, and built up organic forms on the other, with a rapidity that would now seem hardly conceivable.

And yet while all these anomalous things went on, the same laws held that now are operative; and a true doctrine of uniformitarianism would make no unwonted concession in conceding them all—tho most of the embittered geological controversies of the middle of our century were due to the failure of both parties to realize that simple fact.

And as of the past and present, so of the future. The same forces will continue to operate; and under operation of these unchanging forces each day will differ from every one that has preceded it. If it be true, as every physicist believes, that the earth is a cooling globe, then, whatever its present stage of refrigeration, the time must come when its surface contour will assume a rigidity of level not yet attained. Then, just as surely, the slow action of the elements will continue to wear away the land surfaces, particle by particle, and transport them to the ocean, as it does today, until, compensation no longer being afforded by the upheaval of the continents, the last foot of dry land will sink for the last time beneath the water, the last mountain-peak melting away, and our globe, lapsing like any other organism into its second childhood, will be on the surface—as presumably it was before the first continent rose—one vast "waste of waters." As puny man conceives time and things, an awful cycle will have lapsed; in the sweep of the cosmic life, a pulse-beat will have throbbed.

XI
STAR CHARTS

THE charts here presented show all the constellations visible from middle latitudes of the northern hemisphere at one sweep. To avoid confusion, only the brighter stars are shown. After one has learned to recognize a few of the brightest, it is comparatively easy to go on to those of lower magnitudes. Three groups of stars known to everyone are the Big Dipper, the Pleiades, and the Belt of Orion. If one recalls that the two "pointer" stars (known to everyone as pointing to the pole star) lie almost on the 11-hour meridian, this will serve as a sort of point of departure from which to reckon. The northernmost star of the Belt of Orion lies on the celestial equator, at about five and a half hours right ascension. The two stars making the rim of the Big Dipper are about ten degrees apart, and the pointer nearest to the pole star is about 28 degrees from the pole. Other "yardsticks" will suggest themselves as you become familiar with the stars.

If you study the charts somewhat attentively, noting constantly the right ascension and declination of each important star, and in general terms the bounds of the more important constellations, your progress will be much more rapid than if you merely view the stars at random, without reference to their specific locations.

Since, owing to the earth's orbital movement, each constellation necessarily shifts round the entire circuit of the heavens in a year, the monthly shift is one-twelfth of

360 degrees, or 30 degrees. A constellation that is directly overhead, or on the meridian at nine P.M., July 31st, will be 30 degrees west of the meridian at the same hour of August 31st. Once you have located the constellations for any month, you will always know where to look for them by bearing in mind the meridional position.

Of course the constellations necessarily swing westward around the circle of the heavens in 24 hours, owing to the earth's rotation. And it is obvious that the shift for two hours on any given night will equal the monthly shift due to the orbital motion. That is to say, if you find a constellation directly on the meridian at nine P.M., you will find it 30 degrees west of the meridian at eleven P.M. of the same night. When you have learned to gage angular distances, you will know where to look for the stars in accordance with these shifts, and you will be in the position of one who in looking up to the heavens feels among old friends.

No other single consideration will enable you to obtain this degree of proficiency with anything like the facility that will result if from the outset you pay attention to the right ascension and declination — in effect the longitude and latitude—of the stars whose acquaintance you wish to cultivate.

A word about the use of the charts. The first-magnitude stars are guide marks that should always be looked for in locating the constellations. If in doubt, squint through nearly closed lids, and the lesser stars will disappear, the big ones standing out. At twilight of dusk or dawn the first-magnitude stars are visible when the sky is otherwise blank. At night a flashlight enables you to use the charts to advantage in the open.

Ordinarily face south, and hold the book upright, or even above the head, until a few prominent guide stars are located. In looking at the circumpolar view, it will be convenient to face north, and hold the book upside down. The Big Dipper will give the clue to the positions of the northern constellations.

It will be seen that on the dark backgrounds of the star charts, the white images of stars are of varying sizes, somewhat in accord with the varying magnitudes of the stars themselves.

About one hundred of the brightest stars are also marked with radiating points, or *rays*, that vary in number. I have endeavored thus, with the aid of the burin, to give a pretty accurate notion of the gradation of magnitudes — in particular among the two-score *Second-Magnitude* stars, which are very important guide marks.

All stars of technical magnitudes 1.50 to 2.50 are said to be of "second magnitude." But the range of brightness between Castor (1.58) and Mintaka (2.48) is very notable. It seemed worth while to subdivide the group on the charts. The system of *rays* makes this feasible. The plan adopted is this:

Four-ray stars are between magnitudes 1.50 and 2.00; *three-ray* stars between 2.00 and 2.25; and *two-ray* stars between 2.25 and 2.50. This completes the roster of *Second-Magnitude* stars, of which about forty sentinel the northern sky. A few fall on light backgrounds in the circumpolar charts, and are lettered but not rayed. The others will be recognized and appraised at a glance.

The *First-Magnitude* stars, aggressively large and with multiple rays, are of course even more conspicuous.

There remains a scattered group of smaller stars breveted with *one ray*. These are the forty-odd leaders among stars of *Third Magnitude* — those between magnitudes 2.50 and 3.00. The remaining third-magnitude stars (3.00 to 3.50) and the fourth-magnitude stars (3.50 to 4.50) are shown as rayless dots of variant sizes.

As a further aid to identification, the stars of magnitude brighter than 2.75 (with a few omissions) are tabulated below in the sequence in which they cross the meridian. You may locate them on the charts by following the hour-circles sequentially from right to left (west to east); beginning at 0 meridian, or hour, which is also hour XXIV, at the right side of charts 7 and 8.

It will be seen that declinations (latitudes) are also given, so that the precise location of each star on the appropriate chart is as simple as the location by longitude and latitude of, say, your home city on a terrestrial map.

The right ascensions and declinations show "mean positions" for 1930, as given in *The American Ephemeris and Nautical Almanac* — seconds being omitted.

A sweep of the charts under guidance of this tabular census of rayed stars will prepare you for rapid progress in the identification of the stars themselves.

THE BRIGHTEST STARS IN THE ORDER OF RIGHT ASCENSION

No.	Name of Star	Magnitude	Right Ascension H M	Declination	Chart No.
1	Alpha Andromedæ (Alpheratz)	2.15	0 4	+28° 42'	7
2	Beta Cassiopeiæ (Caph)	2.42	0 5	+58 45	10
3	Beta Ceti (Deneb Kaitos)	2.24	0 40	—18 22	8
4	Gamma Cassiopeiæ	2.25	0 52	+60 20	10
5	Beta Andromedæ (Mirach)	2.37	1 5	+35 14	7
6	Gamma Andromedæ (Almach)	2.28	1 59	+41 59	7
7	Alpha Arietis (Hamel)	2.23	2 3	+23 7	7
8	Beta Persei (Algol) ...... Var. 2.30 to	3.50	3 3	+40 41	10
9	Alpha Persei (Mirfak)	1.90	3 19	+49 36	7, 10
10	Alpha Tauri (Aldebaran)	1.06	4 31	+16 22	7
11	Beta Orionis (Rigel)	0.34	5 11	— 8 16	7
12	Alpha Aurigæ (Capella)	0.21	5 11	+45 55	7, 10
13	Beta Tauri (Nath)	1.78	5 21	+28 32	7
14	Delta Orionis (Mintaka)	2.48	5 28	— 0 20	8
15	Epsilon Orionis (Alnilam)	1.75	5 32	— 1 14	8
16	Gamma Orionis (Bellatrix)	1.70	5 21	+ 6 17	7
17	Zeta Orionis (Alnitak)	2.05	5 37	— 1 58	8
18	Kappa Orionis (Saiph)	2.20	5 44	— 9 41	8
19	Alpha Orionis (Betelgeuse) Var. 0.5 to	1.10	5 51	+ 7 23	7
20	Beta Aurigæ (Menkalinan)	2.07	5 54	+44 56	7
21	Beta Canis Majoris (Mirzam)	1.99	6 19	—17 55	6
22	Gamma Geminorum (Alhena)	1.93	6 33	+16 27	5
23	Alpha Canis Majoris (Sirius)	1.58	6 42	—16 37	6
24	Epsilon Canis Majoris (Adhara)	1.63	6 55	—28 52	6
25	Delta Canis Majoris (Wezen)	1.98	7 5	—26 16	6
26	Eta Canis Majoris (Aludra)	2.43	7 21	—29 9	6

THE BRIGHTEST STARS IN THE ORDER
OF RIGHT ASCENSION
(Continued)

No.	Name of Star	Magnitude	Right Ascension H M		Declination	Chart No.
27	Alpha Geminorum (Castor)	1.58	7	30	+32° 2'	5
28	Alpha Canis Minoris (Procyon)	0.48	7	35	+ 5 24	5
29	Beta Geminorum (Pollux)	1.21	7	41	+28 11	5
30	Alpha Hydræ (Alphard)	2.16	9	24	— 8 21	6
31	Alpha Leonis (Regulus)	1.34	10	4	+12 18	5
32	Gamma Leonis (Algeiba)	2.61	10	16	+20 11	5
33	Beta Ursæ Majoris (Merak)	2.44	10	57	+56 45	9
34	Alpha Ursæ Majoris (Dubhe)	1.95	10	59	+62 7	9
35	Delta Leonis (Zosma)	2.58	11	10	+20 54	5
36	Beta Leonis (Denebola)	2.23	11	45	+14 57	5
37	Gamma Ursæ Majoris (Phecda)	2.54	11	50	+54 5	9
38	Epsilon Ursæ Majoris (Alioth)	1.68	12	50	+56 20	9
39	Zeta Ursæ Majoris (Mizar)	2.40	13	21	+55 17	9
40	Alpha Virginis (Spica)	1.21	13	21	—10 47	4
41	Eta Ursæ Majoris (Alkaid)	1.91	13	44	+49 39	9
42	Alpha Bootis (Arcturus)	0.24	14	12	+19 34	3
43	Epsilon Bootis (Tzar)	2.70	14	41	+27 22	3
44	Beta Libræ (Zubeneschamali)	2.74	15	13	— 9 7	4
45	Alpha Corona Borealis (Alphecca)	2.31	15	31	+26 56	3
46	Delta Scorpii (Dschubba)	2.54	15	56	—22 25	4
47	Alpha Scorpii (Antares)	1.22	16	25	—26 16	4
48	Zeta Ophiuchi	2.70	16	33	—10 25	4
49	Epsilon Scorpii	2.36	16	45	—34 10	4
50	Eta Ophiuchi (Sabik)	2.63	17	6	—15 38	4
51	Lambda Scorpii (Schaula)	1.71	17	28	—37 3	4
52	Alpha Ophiuchi (Ras Alhague)	2.14	17	31	+12 36	3
53	Gamma Draconis (Etamin)	2.42	17	54	+51 29	9
54	Epsilon Sagittarii (Kaus Australis)	1.95	18	19	—34 25	2
55	Alpha Lyræ (Vega)	0.14	18	34	+38 43	1
56	Sigma Sagittarii (Nunki)	2.14	18	50	—26 23	2
57	Alpha Aquilæ (Altair)	0.89	19	47	+ 8 40	1
58	Gamma Cygni (Sadr)	2.32	20	19	+40 1	1
59	Alpha Cygni (Deneb)	1.33	20	39	+45 1	1
60	Epsilon Pegasi (Enif)	2.54	21	40	+ 9 53	1
61	Alpha Piscis Austrini (Formalhaut)	1.29	22	53	—29 59	2
62	Beta Pegasi (Scheat)	2.61	23	0	+27 42	1
63	Alpha Pegasi (Mirfak)	2.57	23	1	+14 49	1

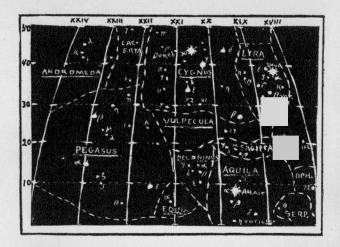

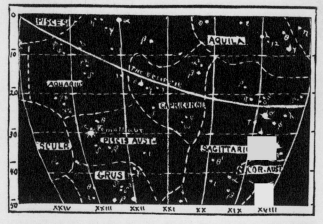

CHARTS 1 AND 2.—The Evening Sky in Autumn. Hour circle XXI crosses local meridian at 9 P.M. September 21, and four minutes earlier each succeeding night.

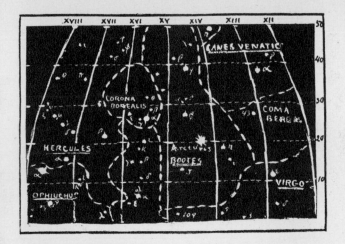

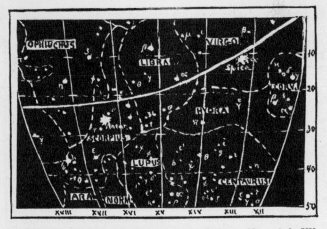

CHARTS 3 AND 4.—The Evening Sky in Summer. Hour circle XV crosses the local meridian at 9 P.M. June 21; an hour earlier July 6; at 7 o'clock July 21; at 5 in the morning February 21.

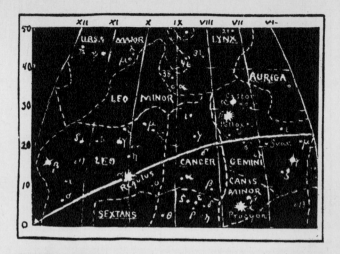

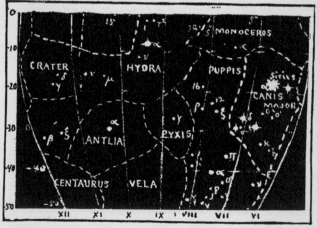

CHARTS 5 AND 6.—The Evening Sky in Spring. Hour meridian IX
is directly overhead at 9 P.M. March 21; at 5 A.M. November 21.

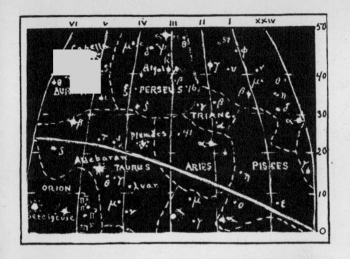

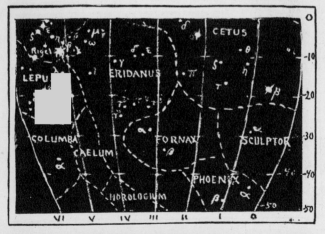

CHARTS 7 AND 8.—The Evening Sky in Winter. Hour circle III crosses the local meridian at 9 P.M. December 21; at 8 P.M. January 6; at 7 P.M. January 21.

CIRCUMPOLAR REGION, HOURS VI TO XVIII

CIRCUMPOLAR REGION, HOURS XVIII TO VI